A Country to Call Home

A Country to Call Home

EDITED BY
Lucy Popescu

WITH ORIGINAL ILLUSTRATIONS BY
Chris Riddell

unbound

First published in 2018

Unbound
6th Floor Mutual House, 70 Conduit Street, London W1S 2GF
www.unbound.com

Original illustrations © Chris Riddell, 2018

Cover artwork © Haymanot Tesfa, 2018
Cover design by Mecob

Text Design by PDQ Digital Media Solutions, Bungay UK

A CIP record for this book is available from the British Library

ISBN 978-1-78352-604-8 (trade pbk)
ISBN 978-1-78352-606-2 (ebook)
ISBN 978-1-78352-605-5 (limited edition)

Printed in Great Britain by Clays Ltd, Elcograf S.p.A.

1 3 5 7 9 10 8 6 4 2

With special thanks to Jeanne Coker, Faz Fazeli, Michaela Fyson, David Holman, Tarek Khlat and Andrew Newton for their support of this book

To all those children in need of
a safe country to call home

Contents

Lucy Popescu
INTRODUCTION

People have moved across land and sea for thousands of years whether in search of food or to trade. Over time, the reasons for migration have evolved. War, cultural or religious persecution, drought and famine are just some of the reasons people flee their native lands to reach safety. Then and now. The survival instinct is strong in us all. It is part of life.

Just imagine if you were forced to leave your home, family and friends, to learn new customs, eat different food, adapt to a harsh climate, speak a foreign language. You're on your own. There may not be a school willing to take you or, if there is, you are told that you are not allowed to study. You live in cramped quarters and have limited food. Or you don't have accommodation, have to sleep rough and beg for food. People shout at you in a language you don't understand and offer little in the way of sympathy. You would be desperate to return home, to everything that is familiar, as soon as you possibly could.

Over half of the world's refugees are children. Many arrive on our shores utterly alone. Some don't make it. Remember that image of Alan Kurdi, the small Syrian boy, just a toddler? His tiny body, face down, washed up on a Turkish beach? The photograph was reproduced worldwide and helped temper the negative media for a short while. It was this image that made me think of putting together an anthology that explores the reality for child refugees and unaccompanied young adults making these harrowing journeys in search of safety. Some of our finest children's writers have contributed stories, poems and flash fiction exploring the reasons people have to flee their homelands, the risks they take travelling in the backs of lorries, the terrifying sea voyages they endure, their arrival and assimilation in a new country, and the harsh confinement of some young asylum seekers in camps and detention centres. Many contributions expose prejudice; others celebrate the incredible fortitude of child refugees, their hopes and aspirations. The image of Alan Kurdi changed hearts and minds and I hope this book will too.

The plight of young refugees is nothing new. Sue Reid and my late mother, Christine Pullein-Thompson, have written historical pieces about crossing borders during periods of turmoil in Eastern Europe. My mum's piece is set just before the Romanian revolution in 1989. It is about a young boy who has to choose between living without fear in Britain or remaining in his repressive native country in order to look after his frail grandmother. Refugees suffer terrible hardship when they are forced to leave their homes and families and are often desperate to return as soon as the situation in their country has improved. Sue's story takes us back to Hungary in 1956, when the revolution was crushed by the Soviets. Sue was fascinated to learn that children were among those who fought the Soviet tanks. Her story reminds us of a time when refugees, in spite of the huge number that escaped, were made very welcome by the West and countries elsewhere.

Bali Rai writes about a young Syrian orphan's petrifying journey by boat. Anna Perera imagines what it is like to be a Sri Lankan child in the middle of a war zone. Michael Morpurgo describes the flight of an Afghan boy and his mother who are smuggled across countries in the back of a lorry. As these pieces prove, there have always been people in need of safety – it's just the geography, government or conflict zone that changes. That's why I've included an interview with the wonderful children's writer and illustrator Judith Kerr, who escaped from Hitler's Germany with her parents and brother in 1933 when she was nine years old and has been writing children's books since the 1960s. Brian Conaghan makes this connection in his eloquent poem which opens the anthology, told from the points of view of a Polish and a Syrian refugee. And Simon Armitage underlines the timelessness and circular nature of displacement in his powerful poem which closes the anthology.

Moniza Alvi writes from personal experience about her family's flight after the partition of India and Pakistan, but in her poem 'Exile' she writes about refugees from Sarajevo. Kit de Waal has written a piece of flash fiction inspired by the same photograph of Alan Kurdi that moved me. Some contributors – David Almond, Sita Brahmachari, Fiona Dunbar and Miriam Halahmy – imagine what it is like to be a young refugee adapting to life in a foreign country. Peter Kalu writes from the perspective of an asylum seeker working in a kitchen and living in limbo. When you have no rights, no benefits and no ability to earn money legally, inevitably grey areas open up. It is easy to exploit those desperate for employment, as Eoin Colfer's short story about young factory workers demonstrates. Tracy Brabin explores what it is like to have your home raided at dawn by immigration officers and, together with Michael Morpurgo, writes of children imprisoned in the UK's Yarl's Wood detention centre, while Jon Walter explores the reality for children marking their days in an Australian detention centre on Christmas Island. Britain and Australia both employ the cruel policy of indefinitely detaining asylum seekers while their applications are processed or they await the result of an appeal. This means that those seeking refuge can be incarcerated for months or even years. Asylum seekers are often referred to as 'aliens', and S. F. Said examines this in his wonderful sci-fi story, an extract from his latest novel, *Phoenix*.

It's not all doom and gloom. Hassan Abdulrazzak has written a touching love story between a Syrian boy, a Mexican girl and a rescue dog called Frida. Adam Barnard has contributed a compelling article about a therapeutic activity holiday where teenage refugees learn to laugh again. Tony Bradman offers an uplifting message at the end of his poem, 'Words', and Patrice Lawrence and I write about finding solace in music.

I hope that *A Country to Call Home* will build on the success of *A Country of Refuge*, my previous anthology about asylum seekers and migration featuring the work of celebrated British and Irish writers, and gain new readers. I'm delighted that many of the contributors to *A Country to Call Home* portray experiences that are so different from their own lives. When we start to consider what it must be like to flee our home and arrive in another country, without friends or family, we can better sympathise with those people for whom this is a reality. They are just like us, but circumstances in their own country have proved intolerable. Empathy engenders change. If we can't put ourselves in others' shoes, we lead narrower lives. We are richer for recognising and celebrating our similarities and our differences. I hope after reading the anthology that you will want to show your support for young refugees and asylum seekers the world over, and extend the hand of friendship to all those struggling to find somewhere safe to call home.

Lucy Popescu
January 2018

JUST ANOTHER SOMEONE

Brian Conaghan
JUST ANOTHER SOMEONE

There goes my home:
My play, my school, my heart smiles
The trees we climbed
Sea we swam
Place that tells me I was once a child.

> There goes my home:
> My everything, my canvas, my first kiss
> Waiting until Mama and Papa
> Fell asleep
> To run, find, feel his lips.

There goes my home:
My voice, my faith, my inner safe
The hunger shared
A future craved
Across the horizon we gazed, we waved.

> There goes my home:
> My hope, my peace, my dream desire
> Ears on tales
> From wrinkled tongues
> The tastes, the scents, the foreign guns.

We could no longer remain.

                      We could no longer remain.

They squeezed us onto
A boat.

                      They squeezed us onto
                      A train.

A bend in the moon
Guides our rust rig and fear
We hold on for dear life anew
In pitch-black
With only yellow eyes in view.

                      I closed my face
                      To pray the cries and howls away
                      We moved
                      To the rhythm of the rail
                      Mothers, fathers, the young, the old.

Terrified.

                      In terror.

Through dawn's tears and mist
They float past
Like driftwood.
Too many orphaned
Or widowed
Or wish to be.

We arrived
I lost Papa's hand...
Scraped my feet
And gripped the earth of my land.

I am the same as you.

We are the same.

I have a mother.

I have a father.

I have love.

I have love.

I surrender myself to memories.

All I have is memories.

We arrive
With a new title: refugee.
Legions of kindness battle
With those of cruelty
Spits with embraces
We are nobody in no place.

We are nobody in no place
Branded under foreign flag
Without art
Beauty
Humanity
A life suppressed.

Let's make the best of it.

          Let's try to make it.

One day I might return
To my play, my school, my heart smiles
When things will
Be changed.

          I fantasised of returning
          To that first kiss
          His lips
          His skin
          My everything.

When I will kiss my sisters.

          Breathe Mama and Papa.

Inhale the sea, hug the horizon.

          Touch joy at the tales being sung.

Sleep again.

          Feel again.

Smell again.

          Laugh again.

Rid myself of this loneliness.

          Allow my heart to bite.

Cycle.

Paint.

Sing.

Run.

Be recognised...

Be recognised...

My name is Nizar Qabbani
Sixteen, orphan, refugee.
I fled Syria.

My name is Hanna Yellen
Artist, orphan, refugee.
I fled Poland.

In 2017

In 1939

I am someone.

I am someone.

THE MERMAID

Bali Rai

THE MERMAID

'Are you OK?'

The woman was blonde; the tallest I had ever seen. She stooped to bring her face level with mine.

'You speak Danish?'

'Some,' I replied.

'*English?*'

'More.'

She sat beside me, her skin pink with cold.

'It's freezing out here,' she said in English. 'Where is your coat, your scarf?'

'I left them...'

'At home?'

'I live with my uncle's family,' I told her. 'It is not the same thing.'

The woman removed her lilac scarf and wrapped it around my neck.

'How did you get here?' she asked.

'I walked – from Nørrebro...'

I pointed to the little statue sitting on its rock at the harbour shore. I had been careful not to get too close to the water.

'I am like her,' I added. 'A mermaid, far from home...'

She seemed confused.

'I am Bettina,' she told me. 'Would you like some coffee? Food, perhaps?'

My stomach growled and Bettina smiled.

'I heard that,' she said.

She stood and held out her hand.

'Come, little mermaid,' she said. 'There are no princes here today.'

A single tear rolled down my right cheek.

'No,' I replied. 'No princes...'

Papa looked forlorn.

'Whatever happens, keep hold of my hand,' he whispered in English. 'You must not let go, no matter what.'

I nodded.

'Yes, Papa,' I told him. 'I will not let go.'

The beach was crowded with others just like us, and all were anxious. I had no idea of the time, because it meant nothing at all. All that mattered was moving forward, reaching our next goal. Leaving what came before, further and further behind, no matter the pain, no matter the cost.

Three smugglers stood guard over us, carrying guns and torches. A fourth separated us into groups. A woman held her infant daughter to her breast. The wailing child was swaddled in a ragged blanket, over which plastic bags had been wrapped.

'Please!' the woman sobbed. 'My daughter is cold. How long must we wait?'

She had travelled with us since Beirut, and my heart ached for her.

'Papa – can we give her some clothes?' I asked, even though I knew we could not.

Papa shook his head, his eyes watering.

'No,' he replied. 'I am sorry.'

We had nothing ourselves, yet still the guilt gnawed at me. I fought back my own tears. Papa had told me to be strong, to think of Mama and my little sister, Sana. I did that now, as the wind whipped around us and the temperature continued to fall. It did not help.

A young man asked which language we were speaking. Papa did not answer. He had been an English teacher in Damascus, and taught my sister and me from childhood. Since leaving our home, we had conversed in Arabic only when necessary.

'Speaking English will allow us some privacy,' he'd told me. 'We can trust no one.'

One of the smugglers flashed his light three times.

'The boats are coming!' said another.

The fishing trawler was overcrowded and I could not move. Papa held me in his arms, both of us still soaked from the short trip from the beach to the boat. The smugglers had rowed us out on rubber dinghies before forcing us aboard the larger vessel. Now, as the wind grew steadily worse, we rocked and swayed in the open, in almost darkness.

Before this, I had always loved the sea. Each summer, Papa would pack Sana and me into the car as Mama fussed over food and clothes. He would drive us across the border into Lebanon, to visit with friends in Sidon, right on the Mediterranean. We would visit the sea castle, and eat ice creams by the fountain in Nejmeh Square, or spend entire days at the public beach. As Sana giggled and splashed about in the water, I would close my eyes and dream of mermaids, just like Ariel in my most-treasured DVD...

I awoke suddenly to shouting and barked orders. I do not know how long I had slept, nor did it matter. Sleep without peace was useless. Yet, it was all I had known since we'd fled our home.

'What is happening, Papa?'

'The smugglers are panicking,' he whispered. 'They've spotted a patrol boat.'

'Patrol…?'

Papa nodded.

'They look for smugglers,' he explained. 'If the smugglers are caught with us, they will go to jail and we will be returned to—'

'But—'

'Ssh!' said Papa. 'Stay alert, my daughter.'

He turned to another man and spoke in Arabic. The man seemed to agree with Papa, and the two of them pulled other men closer. Soon all were discussing something in hushed tones.

The smugglers began to shout louder and then I heard a splash. A woman screamed for her husband. When I looked up, the smugglers were pushing more people overboard.

'PAPA!' I screamed, as all hell broke loose.

'Come!' Papa ordered, holding out his hand.

We followed others towards the stern, where another rubber lifeboat was fastened to the side. The men began to tug at the ropes, hoping to release the knots. One of them produced a knife. More people joined us, including the mother I had watched earlier. She held her baby more tightly than ever.

'What is happening?' she asked.

'I don't know,' I told her. 'But stay close to Papa and me. Make sure you follow—'

A gunshot drowned out my words. Ten feet away, a teenage boy screamed and clutched at his chest, his fingers bloody.

'GET AWAY FROM THE LIFEBOAT, YOU FILTHY DOGS!'

More gunshots followed, and another man fell dead before my eyes.

'GET AWAY!'

But Papa and the others ignored the warnings. As the

boat began to sway uneasily, I took hold of the woman and pulled her closer. Papa turned and pointed to the sea.

'When the lifeboat drops, jump!' he shouted. 'Do not think, do not look back – just go!'

'But Papa, I—'

Papa took my face in his hands.

'I will protect you,' he said. 'I promise, Nadia...'

The fishing boat creaked and rocked, as more people scrambled towards the stern. The smugglers opened fire again, and then I heard a wrenching sound. The rubber dinghy dropped to the water and began to bounce ferociously.

'NOW!' yelled Papa.

I turned to the woman.

'I will go first,' I told her in Arabic. 'Throw your baby down to me when I am safe.'

The woman's face grew pale. She shook her head over and over again.

'PLEASE, NADIA!' I heard Papa cry out.

Those closest to us began to jump.

'We have no other choice!' I told the woman.

There was no time left. I had to jump too. I held my breath and waited for the yellow dinghy to bob closer to the boat.

'GO!' screamed Papa.

I fell dead centre, onto my face. Someone pulled me aside as another person landed nearby. Still others threw orange life jackets from the deck. Then I saw Papa jump. But the dinghy lurched and he fell into the black water.

'PAPA!' I screamed.

Above me, the woman and her daughter appeared. Only, she did not jump. Instead, her back arched, pushing her midriff forward at an unnatural angle. Blood sprayed from her chest and both she and her daughter fell.

'NO!!!!' I cried, but there was nothing I could do.

Pandemonium reigned. People were still jumping, and those already aboard attempted to row away. Body after body fell into the water, and there was no sign of Papa. The lifeboat began to tip as those in the sea tried to scramble on. I felt my heart thumping within my chest. My legs felt hollow and I began to tumble. Just before I entered the sea, I took hold of a life jacket. I gasped as my head went under and I swallowed salty water. But I kicked my legs and quickly broke the surface, sucking in precious air, trying not to choke.

Then I felt Papa's hand on my shoulder...

I will never know how long we floated in the cold and the darkness. I will only ever remember Papa holding me close, begging me to stay awake. I was so tired, so empty, but he did not give up on me.

'Remember the film,' he whispered. 'Remember the stories we made up. You are Ariel and this water is your kingdom. I will save you, just like the prince in our stories, Nadia. Soon you will reach the shore...'

He pushed me up and took my weight too. Even though I wore the life jacket and not him. I heard screaming and yelling, and saw people begin to lose hope. Many gave up and, when next we looked, they were gone. Bodies floated past us, young and old, male and female, but still Papa kept us alive.

'Papa,' I told him. 'You cannot hold me much longer. Let me go – I can support myself.'

'No, Nadia!' he insisted. 'The day your mother and I chose to create you and Sana, we made a pact with Life. To my everlasting shame, I could not save Sana. Now my job is to protect you, care for you...'

His teeth chattered and he had to force the words out.

'It's too late for Mama and Sana,' he said. 'But they did not die in vain. For them, we will survive. For them, we will rebuild...'

I shook my head as another dead human being floated

past us. What had become of us, of our world? Did our lives really mean so little? I did not want to die this way. This was not the Life I had envisaged. This was not the story I had written for myself. This was not the mermaid I had hoped to become...

When, at last, we heard the boats, Papa whispered the words that will forever live within my shattered heart: 'Hush now, little mermaid, your saviours are coming...'

'Our saviours, Papa,' I said.

Papa tried to smile, but there was no strength left inside him. Whatever energy he had, he'd used to keep us alive. He spat water and began to cry.

'Hush, Papa,' I told him. 'We will soon be saved.'

I heard the remaining survivors calling out to God, praising his name. I did not join them. What little faith I had was lost.

'Remember the good times,' Papa said to me, closing his eyes and taking a deep breath. 'Do not ever forget them. No matter where you go, I will always be with you...'

I felt his grip loosen and I screamed, 'PAPA! PAPA!'

A small lifeboat approached us, its lights cutting through the gloom. The soldiers wore orange life jackets like mine and spoke a language I did not understand.

'Papa!' I shouted. 'We are saved!'

Papa opened his weary eyes. He shivered and convulsed, struggling to keep his head above water.

'I am sorry,' he gasped. 'I cannot go on. Go, little mermaid. Go and be safe...'

He pushed me towards the oncoming boat. Strong hands took hold of me, lifting me to safety.

'PAPA!'

He looked to me one last time, with such love and such sadness. And then he was gone.

Bettina wiped away tears. The coffee shop was packed and warm, the windows steamed over. People discussed friends and life, work and children.

'Oh, Nadia,' said Bettina. 'I don't know what to say...'

'There is nothing to say,' I replied. 'I am no one. I have become nobody. I have no voice, no life, no hope...'

'But you are safe here,' Bettina told me.

'My uncle and his family have been kind,' I replied. 'But I am lost too.'

'You went to the harbour to remember your papa?'

'Yes,' I replied. 'Today would have been Papa's birthday. I wanted to wish him well.'

'And you?' asked Bettina. 'How old are you?'

'Fourteen,' I told her.

'Perhaps one day, you will go home,' she said, taking hold of my hand across the table.

'No,' I replied. 'I am just like the mermaid by the harbour. Stranded far from home. Forever.'

I WANT
THE
TRUTH

Christine Pullein-Thompson
I WANT THE TRUTH

Ion had reached the border. He stood behind a long line of lorries. His own country lay beyond. He could see wooded hills, the dim outline of mountains, acres of yellow stubble, one-storey houses built out of mud bricks; the long straight road to home. He felt like a moth beating against a window, trying to get into a lighted room. The ploughed land was being raked by a slow-moving peasant. The soldiers were in their watch towers. They looked harmless enough, but were certainly ready to kill. He looked at the lorries and knew that they were his only hope. If only he could get inside one and conceal himself. But most of them were State-owned container lorries. There was no way of getting inside them and no room underneath to hide either. There were hardly any cars yet. It was too early for visitors with the dew still wet on the grass. He sat down on the verge and waited. The drivers chatted and smoked, waiting their turn. He could hear laughter coming from the soldiers. Suppose they were the same ones as were there yesterday? Suppose they recognised him?

The lorries moved on, leaving him alone on the verge. The grass was blackened by petrol fumes and diesel oil. Only a hundred metres away, a small girl was watching a flock of geese. What would they do if they caught him? The thought made him tremble. He must not think of it. He would not be caught. There was a lorry parked near him now full of sacks.

He could climb inside and hide. The driver had disappeared in the direction of the frontier, leaving the engine running. For a moment Ion's legs refused to move. Then he bounded across the road and clambered into the lorry. The sacks were empty and smelled of maize. He pulled some over his head and lay down, afraid to breathe. Presently the driver came back laughing. They were all like that, Ion decided, always laughing because they felt so important driving their big trucks, passing the slow-moving oxen, nearly running down old ladies, hooting loudly all the time, frightening horses, leaving a trail of petrol fumes behind them. The lorry was moving now. Ion curled up tightly, his fists clenched so that the whites of his knuckles showed. He felt the lorry stop again. Obviously they were through the first barrier, but still on the wrong side. The soldiers were quick. They laughed and made cheerful remarks and then the lorry moved on, and now the soldiers spoke Ion's language.

'What have you got inside?' they asked, letting down the tailboard. 'How long have you been away?'

Ion held his breath until he felt he would burst.

'Why don't you fold the sacks neatly? Anything could hide under that heap,' asked a soldier.

Ion heard him scrambling into the lorry.

'What should I want to bring in?' asked the driver. 'I'm a poor man.'

'Spies from the West. Records… anything…' He touched Ion's legs. 'And there is something here,' he said. 'I was right. I have a feeling for such things. As soon as I saw this truck I knew it contained contraband goods.'

'A boy!'

'The driver knew nothing about me. It is not his fault, please, sir,' said Ion.

'You'd better come inside,' said the soldier. 'You too, driver.'

'I didn't know. I swear to God I didn't know,' replied the

driver, who was a thin man with very little hair and high cheekbones, a man who looked as though he had worked himself to a shadow. Ion was sorry for him. Perhaps he had a family waiting for him at home. The soldiers might shoot him. *And it is all my fault*, thought Ion.

'You come from our country,' said the soldier with a cap. 'Sit down. What were you doing on the other side?'

Ion was silent for a moment. He knew he must be very careful. He was sitting in an office now, facing an officer who had a moustache and strong hands and didn't smile, though his mouth was full of teeth.

'I crossed by mistake yesterday. I had a lift in a cart pulled by oxen. I fell asleep.'

The officer consulted a list. 'No cart pulled by oxen crossed yesterday,' he said.

'It wasn't here. It was somewhere else. It wasn't a big crossing, I woke up and got out and found myself lost,' said Ion desperately. 'Truly, sir.'

'Get on the phone and check up. Find out if any oxen pulling a wagon crossed anywhere.'

A girl in uniform picked up a telephone receiver. She was quite young and very pretty. Ion would have liked her for a sister.

'You slept then?' said the officer.

Ion nodded. Another man was questioning the driver, who had not been allowed to sit down. There were beads of sweat on the driver's face. He kept repeating, 'I had no idea.'

'Your name, please,' asked the soldier. 'And your address.'

Ion gave his real name and the name of his village.

'Check that,' the officer told the girl. 'See if it exists. And get on to headquarters.'

Ion wondered when they would start to torture him. Nothing would make him tell them about Uncle Fanel. He would stick to his first story. He would not change a single word. He was trembling now. The girl talked to the officer in a low voice. Then she fetched him some biscuits and a cup of coffee. Ion could not look at the biscuits. They made him want to cry.

The lorry driver was still standing. It was very hot in the building. A queue of cars waited outside. The officer nibbled a biscuit.

'How are your relations from England? Did they enjoy their stay with you?' he asked presently. 'Are you sorry they have gone with their four beautiful children?'

'Yes, sir. I liked them a lot. They were very cheerful and loved our beautiful land.'

'You must have crossed with them yesterday, but how?' asked the officer, passing him a biscuit.

'I wandered across. Really. I got in the boot when they weren't looking. They were very, very angry, sir.'

'And they threw you out?'

'They told me to go back.'

'If they had been civilised, they would have brought you back and explained everything.'

'They were in a hurry.'

'First the oxen, then the boot. When are you going to tell the truth?'

In a minute he will torture me, thought Ion. *Please, God, help me. Tell me what to say. Someone help me. Grandpa, if you're in heaven, tell me. Mother, please speak now.* The biscuit had turned to sawdust in his mouth.

'It is all lies,' said the officer wearily. 'If you were escaping to the West, why did you come back?'

'I wasn't. I'm returning home to look after my grandmother. She's very old. I just wanted a ride to the border. I wanted to see what was on the other side.'

'I want the truth,' shouted the officer, banging the table so hard that the coffee jumped out of his cup.

Ion's hand started to shake.

'They were trying to get you out. Admit it.'

'No.'

'You're doing no good,' said the girl. 'You are only frightening the boy. Let me talk to him. He will tell me everything.'

She beckoned to Ion. 'Come and have a wash and some coffee. I have a brother the image of you.'

The driver had disappeared, but his lorry was still parked outside. Ion followed the girl into a room at the back of the building. She fetched him towels and soap. She had fair hair and soft brown eyes. 'I want to help you,' she said. 'You will let me, won't you?'

He didn't want to say anything. He liked her; he wanted to go on liking her. But was she really on his side? He washed, drank the cup of coffee she brought him and ate a sugared bun, and with it strength came back.

'Better?' asked the girl, smiling. 'Now tell me everything.'

'I have. I came here with my English cousins and crossed without them knowing and came back today to return to my grandmother. There is nothing else to say.'

The girl talked sweetly to him; she patted his hand and fetched him another sugared bun and told him that he was a very handsome little boy and that she liked his chic English shirt, which must have come from Marks and Spencer, where the English bought all their clothes. She felt the texture of it and looked at the sandals and the shiny English jeans that were spattered with diesel oil. 'Where is your mother?' she asked.

'The soldiers killed her.'

'And your father too?'

He nodded.

'That is bad,' she said. 'Now you tell the truth or you will end the same way.' And she started to shout at him and bang the table as the officer had done. 'Just the truth, all we want is the truth. You got across the border without being seen. How?'

'In the boot,' said Ion, beginning to cry. 'You were here, but you did not see. You were all here.'

'I was not here yesterday. It was my day off.'

'There was a girl anyway,' he said.

'You want to be shot?'

'I don't mind,' said Ion. 'I only mind for my grandma, who needs me. I don't mind for myself.'

The English in their camper seemed to belong to another world. They could cross frontiers as they pleased. They were free. But as for himself he could not even get back into his own particular prison. He put his head in his hands. *Let them shoot me*, he thought. *It is my own fault for coming back.*

When he looked up the girl had gone. A young soldier shook him by the shoulder. 'It's all right,' he said. 'You can go home.'

'Go home?'

'Yes. Go back to your grandmother. Have you any luggage? I'll take you to the nearest town and give you some money. You can catch a train. Have you ever travelled by train?'

Ion shook his head.

'Don't worry. You'll be all right. I expect your relations wanted you and why not? You are an orphan after all. We don't want any scandal here. You just go home and say nothing, eh?'

Ion nodded.

'That will be the best way for all of us. Let me carry you. You must be very tired,' said the soldier. 'I have a very nice car. You will enjoy the journey.'

Ion wondered where he was really going. Was the soldier speaking the truth or was he being taken somewhere to be tortured or shot, quietly and happily so that the tourists waiting outside would not be upset?

'I can walk,' he said. 'But not with shoes because my feet are covered with blisters.'

WORDS

Tony Bradman
WORDS

When I was young I never thought about
The simple words I often spoke.
'Mother', 'Father', 'Sister', 'Brother',
'Home' – the place I had always known –
All in the language that was my own.

Then I learned some hard new words –
'Bomb' and 'Poison Gas' and 'Death'.
We fled and walked a trail of tears
And found a boat to cross the sea,
Where I learned 'Drowning' and 'Refugee'.

The words kept coming as we travelled on –
'Border', 'Transit Camp', 'No Entry'
And 'Refugees Go Home' painted in red
Above a closed, barbed-wire gate.
A different language, of fear and hate.

Now I am here, still learning words
In yet another foreign tongue.
'School' and 'Teacher' and 'New Home',
'Book' and 'Playground' and even 'Friend'...
But my favourite words are – 'Journey's End'.

GOWSIKA
AUNTIE

CHRIS
RIDDELL

Anna Perera

GOWSIKA AUNTIE

I hate the smell of petrol but have a job in a service station in Essex. One day a woman with spiky brown hair and a ring through her nose was buried in pictures of beautiful hotels, idyllic beaches, tea gardens and heritage sites of my home country, Sri Lanka. She smiled to herself as she turned the pages of the magazine.

It was midnight.

I was tired and waiting to close up.

She was wide awake and dressed in dungarees. A blue tattoo of a bird on her neck.

'Are you Sri Lankan?'

She must have seen me looking at her from behind the counter and I gave her a warm 'Yes.'

'There's a girl at the dentist's who looks a bit like you. Lucky thing, coming from that stunning island.'

I nodded and didn't say a word. It's easier that way. Most people don't know what happened to my country. They come to lie on the pale sand and swim in the perfect sea. Able to visit the places I can't, and while I hid underground during the climax of the war in 2009, they were sunning themselves on Southern beaches, completely unaware of the massacre of innocent people in the north and east of the island. My mind went back.

*

Only Gowsika Auntie and Uncle knew I was in the hole they had dug in the scrub behind the rusty cans and fence posts, beyond the house, water tank and last, fat chicken.

It was dark but not too dark down there.

Not unbearable.

There was just enough room to squash up on the sloping, red earth with my back against the bumpy wall. I wasn't scared. All I had to do was wait until it was safe to come out and thought nothing of it at first. Not even when the rope ladder was fixed and a cloud of dirt with two of Gowsika Auntie's floating grey hairs drifted down.

Coughing at the thought I might swallow one, I scraped my tongue across my teeth.

'A three-year-old, you are, with that face.' Gowsika Auntie peered in and laughed. 'Not thirteen.'

An armful of crunching leaves dropped on top of the branches to disguise the gaps and one slipped through the dark mesh and landed on my knee. It left a smudge of insect saliva. I wiped it off. The world went quiet. Then Auntie sighed a sigh that said, *This isn't going to work.*

'I can't breathe,' I called.

'Now don't exaggerate, Babeta,' she said. 'In an emergency you'll be safe so don't complain.'

When she finished, I could hardly make out the uneven, shadowy earth in front of my eyes but soon it brightened enough to see the delicate lines on my hand.

'You will definitely have a long life,' the local palmist said yesterday when Auntie forced him to come to the house. 'But not an easy one.'

I believed him. Auntie wanted to know if marriage and children were written anywhere but the palmist said nothing about that, just told me to eat more potato patties and drink coconut milk at every opportunity. Nothing else.

'Waste of money.' Auntie shook her head from side to side. 'You're small with tiny bones. No amount of food is going to make you look strong.'

She was disappointed with the reading and I felt sorry for her but sorrier for myself trapped underground, barefoot with knees up, half a loaf of white bread wrapped in Uncle's old blue shirt on my lap. No cakes. No biscuits. Only one plastic bottle of water to drink and nothing to do but listen to the shelling.

Unscrewing the water, I remembered Uncle's warning. 'Try not to eat and drink too much. You don't want to be going to the toilet down there.'

The idea was disgusting and I refused to worry about being seen when I climbed out. They told me not to leave the hole under any circumstances but there was no chance I would obey.

Auntie's shadow in the lattice above my head crowded in as she bent closer. 'Uncle's packing the car tight. It won't be long before we can leave. Don't be afraid, Babeta.'

'When's Pa coming?'

'Later. Now shush. Don't make another sound. I'm going.'

The branches stopped crackling.

The shelling got closer.

When the firing died, another leaf, then another shifted above my head and I listened to footsteps cracking twigs on the path as Auntie hurried to the house, opened the door and slammed it shut. Shutting me down there.

I looked up but there was nothing to see.

Pinpricks of light coming from the makeshift roof reminded me of the morning sunshine through the shutters at home just before the sun boiled over and Amma snapped them tight to keep the house cool.

'Put the book down. Go on. Go out now,' she said that day. The last time I saw my own mother.

I ran down to the stream to play and the planes came in. There were explosions that made me think I was flying through the air. Followed by a deathly hush. When the clouds of dust broke, I saw the white verandah, tamarind and rambutan trees were covered in rubble. The house and road were gone and smelled of burning tyres.

I sat cross-legged on the gritty earth listening to the screaming. I didn't move. Just waited for the crows to eat me up. There was a sort of free space around me. A space no one could see into. I pressed two fingers into my eyes to make me disappear but it felt like someone was shaking my head so I let go, and when I looked up Pa was standing over me.

A cockerel called from somewhere beyond the village and I could almost hear Pa's voice. 'Uncle's house is hidden by trees. You'll be safer there until I can find a way out. The Sri Lankan Army are bombing the whole region. The casualties are growing. Innocent girls are being taken as prizes, unwrapped and used by the soldiers, else you'll be kidnapped by the Tamil Tigers, who are desperate for more fighters. Hopefully, we can leave on Saturday. Until then do everything Auntie and Uncle tell you. I'll be back soon.'

'But they're not my real auntie and uncle,' I complained.

'Trust them. Please, Babeta,' he said.

It was Auntie who came up with the idea of hiding me underground after an evil dream of eyeless soldiers dragging me off and passing me round like ammunition.

'I would never forgive myself if anything happened to you,' she said.

With Pa operating on the injured by torchlight in the bombed hospital, nothing about his promise to come back later felt right.

'Why can't I stay at the hospital with you?' I asked.

'There's no room,' he said.

'I can sleep on the floor.'

'No. Believe me, it's safer here,' he said, and I went from tired and quiet to sad and scared. I knew what would happen. It had already happened to Amma and my best friend and her family. My cousins. Everyone I knew.

Twiddling open the half loaf of bought bread, I folded a slice in two. The smell of plastic wrapping and Uncle's old blue shirt put me off eating, and instead I listened to the sound of tractors and carts lumbering down the nearby, bloodstained road. It was the sound of people leaving with bicycles, wheelbarrows, rusty coils of wire, plastic sheeting, shovels, pots and pans, sacks of rice and bedposts. As much as they could carry to escape the Sri Lankan Army who were pushing closer.

For hours on end, little fans of silver light broke through the mesh. I imagined trees swaying in the sudden breeze up there while I sucked the full moon from every drop in the water bottle cap.

Gowsika Auntie didn't come again. I had a wee, smothered it with dirt and crawled out the moment the bombing stopped. The fence posts and beautiful garden were covered in masonry. There was nothing left but piles of rubble, black stumps of trees, ruts of furniture and the sudden appearance of three glittering jasmine bushes in the neighbour's garden that you couldn't see before.

Rice Pot, the fat chicken with a black ring round one eye, came squawking up, covered in dust, hopping from foot to foot. By the clacking, I could tell she was scared as well as hungry so I picked her up, tucked the firm cushion under my arm to keep her safe and ran round the path that rings the garden. Past the bushes pockmarked with dust to the edge of the low wall, and over to get to the road. It was only then I noticed my yellow dress was stained and torn.

*

Through the mothy grit, a truck full of jackfruit appeared and stopped. A skinny old man with red betel lips jumped out and started crying.

'Quick, get in,' he said. 'The soldiers are coming.'

He said there was nothing left of the hospital. I didn't believe him. I wanted to find my father. Then a plume of grey smoke burst from the gunfire at the end of the street and he picked me up, hid me under smelly cloths, and slung a basket on top with Rice Pot squawking inside; the raffia wobbled as she hopped around and scratched my arms through the rags.

The bombing followed us down the road, people running everywhere. Ordinary people carrying bundles of clothes, food and small children. Nobody was a rebel. Their only crime was being Tamil.

I couldn't see anything and it was hot under the cloths with the basket on top but the man insisted I stay there. He said people were being marched to their deaths. He knew. His brother was a senior army officer whereas he'd married a Tamil girl, who was now dead and buried. His brother told him to get the hell out of the north, keep driving and not look back. Why he stopped for me, I don't know, but that's how I escaped.

When we got to Colombo firecrackers were going off in the streets. They were waving flags of the Sri Lankan lion. The war was over.

The woman in the service station dropped the travel magazine on the counter, picked up a packet of chewing gum and a chocolate bar to add to the petrol bill and shook her head at the nearby newspaper article about the persecution of Rohingya Muslims in Myanmar.

'More horrible news,' she said.

For some reason it just came out: 'There used to be 1.3 million Rohingya in Myanmar. There's only 350,000 left. It's because of the Sri Lanka option.'

'The what? Sorry?'

'Forty countries including Myanmar, Egypt and the USA were given lessons in 2011 by the Sri Lankan military on how to wipe out conflict and ethnic problems by indiscriminate killing. Brutal war crimes. Media blackout. Sri Lanka became the world expert when the civil war ended.'

'Interesting,' the woman said. 'What's your name?'

A madness came over me. 'Gowsika,' I said, and in that moment Amma, Pa, Auntie and all the tortured souls of my country came and stood beside me. They love the service station and the smell of petrol.

Lucy Popescu
WHAT IS FLASH FICTION?

'Brevity is the soul of wit'
– William Shakespeare

Flash fiction is a very short story, microfiction, usually under 1,000 words. Though it is a work of extreme brevity, it still offers character and plot development, including the Six-Word Story; 140-character stories, also known as twitterature; the dribble (50 words); the drabble (100 words); and sudden fiction (750 words). One writer, David Gaffney, refers to flash fiction as 'sawn-off tales'.

The most famous Six-Word Story is often attributed to American writer Ernest Hemingway, known for his spare prose:

For sale: baby shoes, never worn.

And take this lighter example from Lydia Davis:

He says, 'When I first met you, I didn't think you would turn out to be so... strange.'

But don't be fooled into thinking that flash fiction is an easy way to write a short story.

Flash fiction requires a lot of skill. Every word counts. You may not need a concrete plot and detailed characterisation but good flash fiction conveys a specific mood or image, or presents a memorable character.

Look at Kit de Waal's following contribution. She employs all of the senses and in just a few lines gives us a vivid impression of Alan Kurdi's short life. Her use of the second person, 'you', feels as though she is addressing us direct. Her story provokes various emotions, and she creates a sense of his happy home life, followed by a powerful feeling of loss. Finally, she ends with that horrifying image of Alan Kurdi's corpse. There is a powerful message at the heart of this story. Kit manages to achieve all of this in 329 words.

DID YOU SEE ME ?

Kit de Waal
DID YOU SEE ME?

For Alan Kurdi, the boy on the shore

Did you see me in Kobane, running through the square? Did you hear my father's shout? We were laughing, my brother and I, and my father came lumbering after us, his arms outstretched. 'You're too far away! I cannot catch you!' And did you hear my mother's laugh, see her hands clasped together and the something in her eyes she kept only for us?

Did you see us at the end of the day, lying in the shade with our bellies full, did you see me dreaming? If you had touched me then, I would have been warm and damp, soft under your hand.

My father brought home a puppy only weeks before. It ran into the street and under a car and our tears, my brother's and mine, made salty tracks on our faces. 'It was quick,' my mother said. 'He is sleeping now.' But I wanted him to stay, wanted his yellow fur and his black eyes, his rough tongue, his need of me.

You didn't see when the bricks fell and crushed my mother's skull. But we watched my father rub the dust into his hair, his beard, tear his clothes, raise his arms to heaven. He dressed us in our warmest clothes, took bread for the journey, and we had to run to keep up. We waited in the camp, sat at midnight on the hard stones of the beach. Waited again while my father tore crusts for our supper.

On the boat, I felt his arms outstretched around me, mile after mile, even when the sea was angry, mile after mile. Did you see me when the waves bounced me up and away? Did you hear me shout? Did you see me running in the water? 'I cannot catch you!' he wept.

And when you touched me on the beach, I was cold and wet under your hand, the sand in my mouth, the salty sea in my belly.

You only saw me then.

OUR
BRIDGE TO
FREEDOM

Sue Reid

OUR BRIDGE TO FREEDOM

'See you tomorrow,' Laki said.

'See you tomorrow,' Jancsi replied, knowing that he wouldn't. He couldn't look at his friend. By this time tomorrow he'd be far away, maybe across the Austrian border. It was hard to get his head round that. But he couldn't tell Laki. He couldn't tell anyone. That was what hurt most.

This day had come round so fast.

He'd only been told yesterday they were leaving Hungary, but he'd already known. He'd lain awake at night listening to his parents talk in the next room. They didn't seem to realise how easy it was to hear through the thin walls, and they often forgot to whisper. Mostly they talked about what they should do now, mostly when they thought he couldn't hear them.

'We'll have a better life in the West,' his father had said. 'Remember how it felt to be free?' He sighed. Jancsi remembered. How could he not? For one incredible week, before the Soviet tanks had returned in huge numbers to put down the revolution, you'd been able to walk around the streets, saying whatever you liked, knowing that no one would report you to the Secret Police. People who'd been imprisoned for criticising the government were released. It had felt as if sunshine had burst out all over the country.

But Jancsi felt sure that wasn't the only reason they were leaving. Two days ago Oszkár's mother had come round to ask if they knew where her son was. When they shook their heads, she'd burst into tears. Mother had made her sit down and drink some water. 'The Secret Police are everywhere,' she whispered. 'They're arresting everyone they suspect of taking part in the revolution – even boys like my son. I tried to keep him at home, but I couldn't.' She burst into tears again. 'I'm so afraid. What will happen to him? He's all I have left!'

Jancsi squeezed his hands into fists under the table. He saw his parents glance at each other. He looked down.

They knew, of course they did. He was in danger, too!

He'd last seen Oszkár in Corvin Passage, near the freedom fighters' HQ, a firebomb in his hand, ready to throw at the tank that had got stuck in a corner. He, Oszkár and Laki, they'd made a great team. Jancsi had begged to be allowed to throw it in his place. 'Just this once,' he'd asked the older boy. 'Please!'

Oszkár had looked at him, then nodded, and Jancsi had taken the missile from him and hurled it with all his might at the turret. 'For freedom!' he'd bawled. Then he'd ducked down and wrapped his arms around his head, listening to the roar as the tank exploded. He'd come home that day smelling of gasoline and smoke. Luckily Mother hadn't noticed. But she caught him later, stuffing glass bottles and jars under his jersey. They made great grenades. 'What are those for?' she'd exclaimed and locked him in his room until she'd got him to confess. She'd begged him not to go back.

'How would we feel if anything happened to you?' she said. 'Have you thought of that?' She'd cried then. Jancsi hated it when she cried. He hugged her and promised he wouldn't.

Soon after that, the Soviet tanks had rolled out of Budapest. Jancsi and his friends were jubilant. They'd helped send the Soviets packing. But a week later the tanks were back. And this time there were too many to fight.

Jancsi found it hard to get to sleep that night. He couldn't stop thinking about what lay ahead. It was the last night he'd sleep in his own bed. The last night he'd ever see this room. It was almost too big a thought to take in. This had been his home for all his thirteen years. In the dark he could just make out the outlines of the shelves where his books and carpentry tools were stacked. He didn't think much of the books – they were the only books he and his friends were allowed to read. He didn't mind leaving them behind. But he'd take the tools, and the model he was making. He'd worked on it in the cellar where they'd gone to shelter from the Soviet tanks. He'd hoped to finish it by Christmas. Maybe he still would, in his new home. If only he knew where that would be. All he'd been told was that they were going to live in the West. But where in the West, no one seemed to know.

'Jancsi! Wake up. It's time to get up.' Jancsi opened his eyes to find his father shaking his shoulder. Outside the dark was beginning to lift. He must have fallen asleep. It took him a few minutes to gather his thoughts. Then he remembered. Today was the day. He swung his legs over the bed and reached for his greatcoat. He'd not bothered to get undressed, in case the police came. They often arrested people at night. Like when they'd arrested Oszkár's father.

He tiptoed out of the room as quietly as he could, each creak of his feet on the wooden floor making his heart plummet. What if the caretaker heard him? Even though it was very early, he wouldn't put it past her not to be listening at the keyhole. She was the only person in their block who never smiled at him. Jancsi felt sure she was one of Them.

In the kitchen Mother was packing a rucksack with food for the journey. She told him to eat, pushing a plate in front of him. But Jancsi found it hard to swallow anything. Then Father was locking the door and they were outside, stamping feet up and down in the bitter cold. He wished his parents would stop smiling at him, as if they were off on holiday. What was the point of pretending? They were leaving home, for ever. They would never be back. Maybe he'd never see his friends again. As they walked to the station, he made a list in his head of all the things that could go wrong. Each time a danger passed he'd tick it off.

The plan was to take a train to the town where Jancsi's grandparents lived. From there they'd walk to the border with Austria – the nearest country in the West to Hungary. It would only take a few hours, and they should be in Austria by nightfall. If they could find space on the train! As they arrived at the station, Jancsi stared at the forecourt in disbelief. He'd never seen it so crowded. Were all these people fleeing Hungary, too? Like them, they were carrying cases and bags, rucksacks slung over shoulders. Their faces looked tense and anxious. No surprise there – Jancsi had spotted men moving through the crowd, asking to see people's tickets and identity papers, the badge of the Secret Police on their caps. He made himself small and kept his eyes to himself. Good thing it was so busy – he didn't want to get arrested now. He caught the eye of a boy just as the train doors opened. A freedom fighter like him. He turned away fast. Best not show he recognised him.

He didn't know how they managed to get on the train. What a scrum! People shoving and pushing each other, desperate to find room for themselves and their families. That should tell the Soviets something. No one wanted to live in Hungary now they'd come back. It made Jancsi mad. The Soviet invaders should be leaving, not them. He fought his way to a corner and squatted down in it, resting his rucksack on his knees. The train jolted forward, the carriage rocking slightly like an overburdened elephant. The corner of a case knocked his elbow. He winced. How many hours was it till they got there? He'd made this journey many times, visiting his grandparents. He felt the train gather speed. He'd just have to hope all these people weren't going as far as them.

Above him, people talked in low voices. Everyone, Jancsi saw, was trying not to catch anyone else's eye. You didn't know who people were or why they were travelling. Could be informers among them. He heard someone say that the Secret Police were in the next carriage. Jancsi made himself as small as he could. If only the train would go faster! He tried to calculate how long it would be till they arrived. Hours yet. Maybe they'd have to jump off. Maybe they'd have to run for it.

He wished he could stop thinking this was all his fault. Father had said again and again how much better life would be in the West, but Jancsi had seen sorrow in his eyes. Did he really want to leave his homeland as much as he said he did?

His mother passed him an apple and a sandwich. 'Picnic,' she said, using an English word. His father frowned and shook his head.

The journey felt long and tedious. At each stop more people got on than got off. If only his friends were among them. The time would go faster.

His friends would be back at school now. During the revolution all the schools had closed. Now they'd been ordered to open again. How many of his friends would be sitting at their desks this morning? What would they think when they saw his empty seat? What if no one turned up? It would serve the Soviets right.

He stood up to see where they were and caught a glimpse of red-roofed houses. They looked familiar. Must be nearly there then.

The train began to slow down. Father nodded to Jancsi – they'd arrived. The doors opened. Nearly everyone got out. As he climbed down, Jancsi saw guards checking passengers' tickets.

'Just keep walking,' his father said calmly. Father had seen them too. Lots of people began to run, their cases banging against their legs. Jancsi wanted to run, too. 'Remember,' his father said. 'If anyone asks, we're on our way to visit your grandparents.'

Keep going. Don't look round. Look as if you mean to be here.

It was only when they were well clear of the station that Jancsi realised they hadn't been stopped. Another danger to tick off his list.

It felt peculiar to walk down the familiar streets and turn off before they reached his grandparents' house. What would they think when they learned they had left the country?

'We'll leave the main road soon,' Father said cheerily. 'And go cross-country.'

Where we won't run into any roadblocks. Or Soviet tanks.

'And then we'll find a guide.'

What do we need a guide for? Hasn't Father got a map?

He caught the look his parents gave each other. A knot tied itself in Jancsi's stomach. There was something they weren't telling him.

They weren't the only ones who'd chosen this route. Small groups, families with children, older couples, boys and girls like him, had turned off the main road too and were following a track that led across farmland. Out here in the open countryside it was comforting to be among others making their way to the border like them. Some were chatting cheerfully, striding along as if it was an ordinary day and they were out for a walk in the countryside. Others, the elderly, or those carrying small children, needed help. *But remember, you don't know who you can trust.* They may look like refugees, but you couldn't be sure. They'd all heard about the police who pretended to be refugees to pick up people like him and his family. You just didn't know.

Refugees. *Like him and his family.* He was a refugee too now. It was easy to forget that. A refugee had always been something other people were. Someone who had no country to call home. Best not think about that. Not now.

Sleet began to fall, icy drops that blew into his face so that he could hardly see. Jancsi huddled deeper into his coat. Trust them to pick the coldest day. His legs felt numb. They wouldn't hold him up much longer, not at the pace Father kept up. How much further was it to the border? Then, through the driving sleet, not far away, he saw farm buildings huddled together. Perhaps they could stop there and he could sit down. He wanted to sit down so badly.

As if he could read Jancsi's mind, Father pointed at the buildings. 'We'll ask for a guide there.' He smiled through frozen lips at Jancsi. 'Not long now.'

Jancsi didn't reply. He was tired and cold and he wanted to cry. *I mustn't,* he told himself. *It's because of me we're here.*

There were a number of refugees already at the farmhouse by the time they reached it. Father went up to speak to a man in their midst. He returned after a few minutes. 'We're in luck,' he said. 'The farmer is taking a party off to the border in about an hour. He says it's not far.' He sounded happy. 'Until then we can rest.' He pointed at a barn. 'We'll shelter in there.'

Jancsi sat down, his back against a bale of hay, aching legs stretched out. His mother dug into her rucksack, and handed him some sausage. Jancsi thought nothing had ever tasted so good. His father told them what the farmer had said. 'At the border we have to cross a canal. When we're on the other side, we're in Austria. There's a bridge over the canal – it's old and rickety, but there's a handrail.' He smiled. 'Our bridge to freedom! We'll be in Austria tonight.'

It was growing dark as they set off again, walking across frozen pasture in a long straggly line behind their guide. They kept a little way behind the rest. 'It'll be safer,' Jancsi's father said. Jancsi felt his stomach turn over. If only Father hadn't said that!

The moon was already up. It would be nearly full tonight. That would help them find their way, but it could also help others find them. People they didn't want to find them. Like the police. Or border guards. Jancsi kept his eyes on the ground. It was uneven and several times he stumbled. In the moonlight he could see frost sparkling like diamonds on tall grasses and rushes. Beyond them must be the canal. Jancsi wanted to whoop and jump in the air. It couldn't be far to the bridge now.

A distant crack disturbed the stillness. Jancsi tensed, ready for flight. What was *that*?

'Guards! Guards! Go back! Go back!'

People began to run, peeling away from the path. Ahead Jancsi could hear the rat-a-tat-tat of a submachine gun.

He felt someone throw him to the ground as a bullet whistled past.

He lay there, as still as he could, heart pounding. Were his parents all right? *Where are they?* he wondered desperately. He'd brought them into danger! How could he forgive himself if anything happened to them?

He raised his face a few centimetres from the ground. He could hear shouts and cries further ahead. He turned his head cautiously, eyes looking for his parents.

Where are they?

He lay down again, trying to think. What to do now? Should he try and move, or stay where he was? If he moved, he might be seen. If only the moon wasn't so bright. Best lie here, and hope no one found him.

Jancsi didn't know how long he lay there. It seemed to be hours, and then a sudden movement nearby made him lift his head.

'Jancsi!'

Father!

'Are you all right?'

Jancsi nodded, teeth chattering like castanets. Was Mother all right? Where *was* she?

He felt a tear slide out of his eye.

'Jancsi!' His father crouched down next to him. 'Your mother's all right. I'm all right. And so are you.'

'I'm... sorry, Father. It's... it's all my fault.' He tried to choke down the sobs.

'Jancsi.' Father pulled Jancsi close. 'What are you saying?'

'We wouldn't be here if it weren't for me. I feel so... so...' He turned his head away.

'Now listen,' Jancsi's father said, taking Jancsi's hands and holding them tightly between his. 'None of this is your fault. You're a true patriot and I'm proud of you. You did your bit to defend our country from the tyrants who rule us – who ordered tanks to fire on us – their own people! I decided then that I did not want us to live any longer in a country that could do such a terrible thing. I told myself we would find another country to call home – a country where the government treats people with respect. Where we can be ourselves, and live without fear. It is a hard thing to do, to leave your homeland, but I think it was the right thing to do.'

Jancsi nodded.

'Wipe your eyes,' said his father. 'The guards have gone. We were far enough back for them to miss us. We can carry on now. It's not much further to the bridge. We'll cross it soon. And then, Jancsi, we'll be safe!'

It was a smaller group now that made its way to the bridge. There was a watchtower nearby, but no one was in it. Jancsi tried not to think about those who were no longer with them. Almost certainly they'd been marched off into captivity. How awful to get so close only to be turned back. How easily it could have been them.

He made his way cautiously over the bridge, one hand on the rail.

Don't look back! Don't look back! Not till you're safely across.

A few more steps and he'd be in Austria. He'd be free. But what then? Would this country he did not know, whose language he did not speak, welcome them? Or was this only the first step on a journey to find a place they could call home? *A home is more than a place to lay your head.* How long would it be before he would truly feel at home again?

There were boys on the far side of the canal. They smiled at him as he stepped ashore. Next to him, his father knelt and kissed the ground.

Jancsi felt as if something big had rolled off him. Was this how it felt to be truly free? Inside he knew a part of him would always stay in his homeland. But a brighter future lay ahead.

'*Wilkommen in Österreich*,' he heard one of the boys say. What did that mean? He turned to his mother. She put her arm round him. There were tears in her eyes.

'They're saying welcome, Jancsi. Welcome to Austria.'

THE LITTLE RED TRAIN

Michael Morpurgo
THE LITTLE RED TRAIN

Aman

The door of the container opened. The daylight blinded us. We could not see who it was at first.

It was not the police.

It turned out to be the fixer man, and his gang, the same people who had put us in there. They said we could get out if we wanted and stretch our legs, that we were waiting for some other people to join us.

We were in a kind of loading bay with lorries all around, but not many people. We should have run off there and then, but one of the fixer's gang always seemed to be watching us, so we didn't dare.

Only a few minutes later, it was too late.

The other refugees arrived, and we were all herded back into the same container, given some blankets, a little fruit, and a bottle or two of water. They slammed the doors shut on us again and the fixer shouted at us, that no matter what, we mustn't call out, or we'd be caught and taken to prison. We could hear the lorry being loaded up around us.

It was a while, I remember, before my eyes became accustomed to the dark again, and I could see the others.

As the lorry drove off we sat there in silence for a while, just looking at one another. I counted twelve of us in all, mostly from Iran, and a family – mother, father and a little boy – from Pakistan, and beside us an old couple from Afghanistan, from Kabul.

It was Ahmed, the little boy from Pakistan, who got us talking. He came over to show me his toy train because I was the only other kid there, because he knew he could trust me, I think – it was plastic and bright red, I remember, and he was very proud of it.

He knelt down to show me how it worked on the floor, telling everyone about how his grandpa worked on the trains in Pakistan. And, in secret, I showed him the silver-star badge Sergeant Brodie had given me. Ahmed loved looking at it. He was full of questions about it, about everything. He liked me, he said, because I had a name that sounded like his. It wasn't long before we were all telling one another stories. To begin with, Ahmed and me, we laughed a lot, and played about, and that cheered everyone up. But it didn't last. I think our laughter lasted about as long as the fruit and water.

I don't know where that lorry took us, and how many days and nights we were locked up in the container. They didn't let us out, not once, not to go to the toilet even, nothing. And we didn't dare shout out. They brought us no more water, no more food. We were freezing by night, and stifling hot by day.

When I was awake, I just longed to be asleep so I could forget what was happening, forget how much I was longing every moment for water and for food. Waking up was the worst. When we talked amongst each other now, it was usually to guess where we were, whether we were still in Iran, or in Turkey, or maybe in Italy. But none of this made any sense to me, because I had no idea where any of these places were.

Most of them, like Ahmed and his parents, said they were trying to get to England, like we were, but a few were going to Germany or Sweden. One or two had tried before, like the old couple from Kabul who were going to live with their son in England, they told us, but they had already been caught twice and sent back. They were never going to give up trying, they said.

But in the end the stories stopped altogether, and there was no more talking, just the sound of moaning and crying, and praying. We all prayed. For me the journey in that lorry was like travelling through a long dark tunnel, with no light at the end of it. And there was no air to breathe either, that was the worst of it. People were coughing and choking, and Ahmed was being sick too. But he still held on to this little red train.

The smell, I'll never forget the smell.

After that I think I must have lost consciousness because I don't remember much more. When I woke up – it was probably days later, I don't know – the lorry had stopped. Maybe it was the shouting and the crying that woke me up, because that was all I could hear. Mother and the others were on their feet and banging on the side of the container, screaming to be let out.

By the time they came for us and dragged me out of there, I was only half alive.

But I was luckier than little Ahmed.

When his father carried him out into the daylight, we could see for sure that he was dead. Ahmed's mother was wailing in grief. It was like a cry of pain from deep inside her, a crying that I knew would never end for her. I'd never heard such a dreadful sound before, and I hope I never will again. Later that same day, after they had buried him, his mother gave me his toy train to look after, because I had been like a brother to Ahmed, she said.

THE CAMP

The following is an extract from a book-length poem based on a family story set at the time of the partition of India and Pakistan in 1947. Thousands of people were killed in civil unrest and millions were displaced. My grandmother made the crossing from Ludhiana in India to Lahore in the newly created Pakistan, with five of her children. Her eldest son, Athar, a young man who'd been left with the mind of a child as a result of a childhood accident, disappeared during the crossing, never to be found again. It was the fate of many children and vulnerable adults at that time. My grandmother and her family spent some months in a refugee camp outside Lahore. I imagine it is here that she finds out that her son is missing...

Moniza Alvi

Moniza Alvi
THE CAMP

A vast parody of a city.

Almost featureless.
Teeming, but not bustling.

Children climbed trees
to see where the camp ended.

Tents – and patchwork shelters
of sheet metal, rags and bamboo.

Her temporary home – precarious
yet somehow enduring.

Ludhiana, a lifetime away.
Lahore, just out of reach.

Ragged ocean.
Oh to sail swiftly to the other side!

Where would they end up? And when?
And with what?

*

She washed fine-spun salwars,
hung them to dry wherever she could.

Queued for a bowl of flour,
two half-countries inside her.

Rehila, Jamila, Shehana
quarrelled in the cramped shelter,

or under the canopy of a walnut tree.
Carried water, swept the ground.

Cleaned their nails with twigs
to pass the time.

The nothingness was palpable –
you could pluck it from the air.

A boy took a message to the boundary line.
A daredevil pleasure.

Ahmed missed his older brothers:

Tariq in colder, safer,
distant England.

Athar on the second bus,
soon to join them.

*

Holes in shelters.
Holes in families.

The losses
        trickled out,

poured out,

in the queues, in huddles
around the fire:

Father handed his wallet over.
Somebody hit him.
He bled to death.

Her eyes are sunken.
Her hands, withered.
A fishy smell.
The doctor says it's cholera.

Losses mounting on losses.

And the good fortune:

They warned us... They hid us...
Surely they were angels sent from Allah!

✻

The Housing Project – any news?

Any news? they demanded of each other,
of the police guards,
of the overarching sky.

Time flowered,
        flowered and died.

✻

And now, having come so far,
I'll press on (as she couldn't press on)

and imagine it was here she found out
(indelibly here)

that there was to be no smooth return –

*

We're sorry, they said,
the friends of friends.

So very sorry –

He isn't with us –

He disappeared at –

He vanished between –

The last time we saw him –

We did what we could –

Sorry. We're so very sorry.

*

And at dusk
his name sounded
in the mile-long roll call of the missing:

        brothers
        sons
        aunts

fathers
daughters,
especially
daughters

missing.

Deebas, Daras,
Kasheebas, Kalsooms,
Bhakirahs, Mairas, Baheras,
Yasmeenas, Mahruns...

Daughters missing.

Athar – missing.

*

And there was forever someone
who thought they'd seen them
or knew someone, had a brother
or an uncle or a mother-in-law
who had seen, or had heard
something –

seen Athar
or someone just like him.

So you thought you saw him.
Where?
Tell me again.

*

Why did I...?

Why didn't they...?

A young man so doubly lost.

Knowing no better,
had he wandered off?

Would people be kind?

The darkness fell,
swooped, as darkness does.

DAWN RAIDERS

Tracy Brabin
DAWN RAIDERS

I must've fallen asleep because suddenly I'm flying. Swooping high above the land below. Lush green mountains, huge grey quarries gouged into the earth with little brown insect men digging out the coltan, the wide muddy Congo River cutting lazily into the earth. To one side I hear shouting, *Julienne, Julienne*, but I don't look. This is too nice. The shouting gets louder. I fly higher, the sun warming my face, but then, as if from nowhere, there's a cold draught. The air starts to vibrate as if I've been caught in turbulence from a passing fighter jet, knocking me off balance. I try and shrug off the invisible force but it's getting stronger. I bank to the left, then to the right, but I've taken it too sharply, whoa, I'm tumbling head over heels, argh, falling... falling through the air, picking up speed, help, help me...

My eyes spring open and my chest rises and falls as I realise it was a dream. I slow my breathing and stretch out in relief, then curl back into a ball, pulling the blankets round me like an oversized baby. My tummy rumbles and I remember I didn't have anything to eat last night. It's still dark so I check the time on the clock by my bed. Five thirty. Too early to get up just yet. That's when I feel particles in the air stinging my nostrils, spiky, brittle and hot with fear. I rest on my elbows. Something's not right. In the gloom, I make out Beti sitting up, clutching her giraffe to her chest, her white nightie making her look like a ghost. She's staring at me terrified, whispering my name.

'Beti? Y'OK?'

'Can't you hear?'

'What?'

'Them.'

'Who?'

'Them. They've come back.'

I strain to hear; out in the street there's a slam of van doors. Voices whisper urgent instructions and serious feet pound cold hard concrete.

'It'll be someone doing an early morning flit, not paid their rent,' I say, desperate for her to be wrong.

'No. It's them.'

Beti throws back her covers, slips on her once-cream dog-head slippers and creeps towards the door.

'What you doing?'

'Going to wake Mum.'

'Cos some nutter's moving? Seriously, Beti. Don't. They won't thank you for it.'

'Don't care—'

'Beti.'

'We've got to do something.'

'Okay, stay here. I'll have a look.'

I kneel up and look out of our bedroom window, which opens out onto the walkway. It used to be that anyone could bop up and knock on your door but when the council did the renovation, they increased security. Now there's a reception and you have to be buzzed in. A metal fan of spikes rests on the top of the wall to stop anyone climbing in from the street.

I carefully pull a corner of the blanket away from the rusty nail holding it in position. Dad put clingfilm across the window last year to keep out the worst of the cold, so even without the blanket the view's a bit blurred but I can still see shapes. To my left I can see Beti's old doll buggy, too dirty to come into the flat, and to my right, Dad's wellingtons and Mum's geraniums. All is as it should be. I heave a sigh of relief, turn back to Beti and smile.

'See. Nothing.'

The smash of splintering wood makes us both jump. Beti stifles a scream as shadows flicker past the window, darkening the room. From the sound of it, someone's kicking our front door in. I launch myself off the bed and pull on jeans and a T-shirt. My breath puffs clouds of steam into the chilly early morning air as I head to the door, but Beti grabs me by the wrist.

'I'm scared.'

I turn and paste on a reassuring smile, trying to dull the panic in my voice. 'Don't be. It'll be Psycho Jonno come to the wrong flat again. You know what he's like. Too many beers he thinks this is his flat. Remember last Saturday? When he swore we'd kidnapped his mum—?'

'And we were experimenting on her.'

'Yeah. It'll be him. Don't worry. Now stay here, OK?' And she would have done had we not heard that terrible scream. A scream just like last year's scream.

It was a gorgeous summer's day. Twenty-nine degrees and not a cloud in the sky. Me, Grace and Hanife had been swimming at Park Road Lido. The fact that it's open-air makes it really good fun and swimming's a great way to keep up our training. We all play for Haringey Under-16 Girls' Football team. Hanife's left back, I'm centre half and Grace is in goal. Normally you have to pay to use the lido but we've never any money so we always climb in over the turnstiles. The only downside is, once you're in, you have to keep hiding under towels, or run to the loo so the woman from the ticket desk doesn't see you when she does her pool patrol.

When I got back on the estate, it was almost dark but there were still gangs of kids fighting water wars with Super Soakers (99p – 99p Shop) and Water Pistols (2 for 99p – 99p Shop), desperate for this lovely day to last forever. Up on the walkway, I could see Crazy Coleen's Irish tricolour flag flapping out of her window. She was singing her favourite summer song, The Dubliners' 'God Save Ireland' – 'me ole' rebel song' she always called it. Normally officers from Haringey's antisocial behaviour department would've been round, but maybe they were all sunning themselves as well 'cos she'd really built up steam and was singing at the top of her voice. I got out my key just as her door swung open.

'Well, well, look who it is. My little pal Georgie Best', she slurred with a grin.

Apparently George Best had been an amazing football player in the sixties and Coleen was in love with him. She was wearing yellow rubber gloves and holding a duster. 'How's it going?'

'Fine thanks. Nice singing', I said, making her smile.

'It's the sun', she replied. 'Us Irish, one sniff of a hot sunny ray, we can't help but break into song.' I laughed as she leaned towards me, her Little Bo Peep blonde plait wig (a recent replacement for her short pink one with the asymmetric fringe that some kid set on fire with a firework) slipped slightly off-centre.

'Now, a little birdy has told me that today might just be your birthday. Well, here's a couple of quid and don't tell your Da', she whispered, grinning from ear to ear, shoving a five-pound note into my pocket. (Maybe five pounds isn't much for some, but for me, it's a shed-load and I was really grateful.) I said thank you and she smiled and went back inside, her good deed done for the day.

I could hardly sleep that night it was so hot and I'd got up to get a glass of water from the kitchen when suddenly, out of nowhere, our front door crashed off its hinges and four beefy blokes in uniform fell into our living room. They were all shouting, 'Don't move,' 'Police,' 'Immigration,' 'Get down,' like they were from some crappy Channel Five reality TV show. Why couldn't they have just knocked on the door like normal people? Mum and Dad tried to keep calm but when one of them said we were being forcibly returned to the Democratic Republic of Congo on a plane to Kinshasa, leaving in the morning, everyone started to get upset. Mum and Dad grabbed pants and shirts (we've only one bedroom so Mum and Dad sleep on the sofa bed). Mum was wearing her sleep T-shirt. It was well short and she had to keep pulling it down so's not to show too much leg. I helped Dad on with his shirt (he's a bad arm from getting beaten up in a refugee camp when I was little) and he kept trying to talk to the men, explain that we'd made an appeal to the court and that he could sort this out if only they'd let him use the phone. But no one cared. They just kept saying, 'Get your things,' and, 'Find your passports.' They'd a job to do and they were going to do it, whatever. When one of the men said, 'You've got ten minutes,' Mum got a bit hysterical saying they'd have to kill her before she'd go back to the Congo. Beti was really scared so Dad said the usual stuff adults say when they want to reassure kids – 'We're going to be all right, everything will be OK.'

Well, he was wrong. Seriously, massively, humongously wrong.

Yarl's Wood. Sounds nice, doesn't it? Green. Friendly. Well, let me tell you, it's not. It's Hell's Waiting Room and every asylum seeker dreads it. Nowadays, kids aren't allowed to be put there, but last year, it didn't matter how old you were; if they were sending you home, that's where they'd put you.

From the outside, the barbed wire and security guards made it look like a prison. A warden (a woman with so many chins she could pass for a walrus) showed us into the 'family' room. A total joke if ever I saw one. Family? It was a room half the size of our kitchen. Good for a family of Borrowers maybe. When Mum pointed out that there were only three single beds, The Walrus smiled, like she was making a joke, 'Well, you're off in the morning, I'm sure your girls won't mind bunking up for one night, eh chickedees?'

I could tell Mum was struggling not to punch her in her fat, melty face.

'So,' she went on, her neck wobbling with the vibrations, 'if you'd like to leave your things here and come with me to the doctors, we'll make sure you're all well enough to travel.'

Not knowing what else to do, we followed her down a pale blue corridor into a small windowless room filled with orange plastic chairs and a large brown desk. A pot plant had lost the will to live and was slumped over in a corner like a drunk weeping willow. A grey-haired woman in a striped suit behind the desk checked through sheets of paperwork. Her half-rimmed glasses perched on the end of her nose made her look beakish, like a judge with a serious case of dandruff. Without asking our names, where we lived or what we did, she just waved a box of tablets in the air, saying, 'Malaria is very serious. Two tablets now, two this evening, then one every day for a month after you arrive in Kinshasa. You mustn't forget.'

No one said anything. We just sat there. From outside somewhere, officers shouted instructions and doors slammed shut. Dad started crying. Well, I thought he was crying but he wasn't. He was laughing. Really hard, like he'd just heard the best joke ever.

'You find this amusing, Mr Kizende?' the doctor said, her mouth pinched smaller than a cat's bum at the vet's.

'No, no. It's just. All this care so we don't get malaria. You send us back, I'm not going to live long enough to finish the packet.'

I looked at Mum, she looked at Beti, and as one we all burst into giggles. The more the doctor and The Walrus glared, the funnier it was. Like being in assembly at school. It's impossible not to join in. We couldn't stop. We were The Laughing Kizendes, the happy asylum seekers. The Family that Sees the Funny Side of Everything.

Annoyed, the doctor pushed back her chair and marched to the door. 'If you don't mind,' she said tartly, pushing her pen into her top pocket, 'I've better things to do than listen to laughing hyenas.' If I'd been anywhere else, she'd have got a right mouthful for that but I was with Mum and Dad so I bit my tongue.

Back in our box-room, it was as if all that laughter had sucked the life out of us. We were exhausted. Mum and Dad tried to cover up how frightened they were, making jokes and kissing us, but I could tell they were petrified.

With nothing else to do, we decided to go to bed. Sliding under the thin grey sheet, I was glad we had to share. We were together. It must've been a couple of hours later when I woke up, boiling hot. Beti was like a super-charged hot water bottle and sweating like a pig. I pulled back the covers to let in some air and it was like something from a horror film. Her mouth was matted with gunk and her eyes had rolled back into her head. I must've screamed because in a flash, Mum was there, shaking her.

'Beti! Beti darling. It's me. Wake up.'

Beti started coughing sickie foam in horrible little jerks.

'Joseph! Joseph! We need a doctor. Now.'

The doctor was Indian, tall and thin with fine brown hair swept over his bald patch. He looked so tired the bags under his eyes had bags all of their own.

'Your daughter has had a powerful reaction to the malaria medication, Mr Kizende.' Dad nodded, desperate. 'So I shall be recommending they make arrangements for you to return to your home to give her time to recover.' Mum and Dad looked at each other in disbelief.

'Home?' Mum squeaked.

'This child is far too sick to travel. Repatriation will be postponed.'

The Walrus tried to speak but the doctor glared her into silence. 'This child is sick. She cannot fly.'

Dad shook the doctor's hand till it nearly fell off, but the man just nodded, impassive, as if to say 'we're not all bad, you know', and that was that.

We weren't going to the airport, we weren't going to the Congo, we were staying where it was safe. London. Never had the thought of school felt so sweet. We had dodged a bullet and Beti was the shield. Her puny, feeble immune system had saved our lives. She paid the price for it, though. For weeks afterwards, every night, she wet the bed, and without a drier, spare cash for the laundrette or extra sheets, it couldn't carry on. That's when she started going to the animal shelter in Wood Green. Caring for animals has been proven to help victims of post-traumatic stress disorder according to Mum and it worked. A few weeks stroking abandoned puppies stopped it. Deep down, I reckon it was all a bit of 'attention-seeking behaviour'. I mean, think about it – a *disorder*? Why can't she be just pissed off like the rest of us?

Well, that was over a year ago now and here we are again. I take a deep breath and open the bedroom door.

'Don't leave me,' Beti says, squeezing Giraffe tight to her chest, grabbing my arm.

'I won't,' I say, my eyes on the door. 'But get dressed.'

Beti nods and wriggles out of her nightie, grabbing her favourite dress (Hello Kitty, £4.99 – Primark) from a pile of dirty washing. I pull on socks and trainers. Dressed, she stands to attention, awaiting instruction. I startle her with a peck on the cheek, whispering, 'Whatever happens, stay with me, you'll be OK.' She nods but I can tell she's scared.

I open the door and we creep nervously down the corridor towards the noise.

The living room looks like it's been hit by a tornado. Blankets and pillows have been scattered everywhere. The pine chair by the table is on its side. Family photos normally on the fireplace are face-down on the rug. A lampshade has been knocked off its stand, exposing a bright bare bulb that sends long shadows up the wall. I clock Meow crouching under the side table, terrified. A loud and ominous thuck-thuck of a helicopter overhead gives the scene a movie-trailer intensity. Mum, in her baggy I ♥ NY T-shirt (50p – school jumble sale), talks on her mobile. A man in uniform sporting a severe buzz cut, probably Home Office, waits politely for her to finish speaking. She's pregnant. No one wants a dead baby on their conscience on top of everything else. By the sofa, Dad, in a vest and boxer shorts, is on his knees, hands tied behind his back with one of the tags you normally find on bags of veg in the supermarket, a square-jawed bloke with huge ears like two fat white satellite dishes towering over him. At the open front door, a woman in a beige mac with bleached blonde hair sees us and smiles. 'Hello girls. Don't worry. Everything is going to be all right.'

Jug Ears yanks Dad onto his feet. 'We're outta here.'

The other bloke, Buzz Cut, nods and gets closer to Mum. 'Mrs Kizende. We need to go. If you could gather your things.'

But Mum's not listening, too busy leaving a message. 'I'm so sorry to have to ring you, Pastor, but the Home Office are here. I tried our lawyer but it's too early. Could you ring them – 0208 444 6405 – as soon as you get this? Please. It's of the utmost urgency.'

Dad is now by the door with Jug Ears rattling through the formalities – 'Mr Kizende, I am arresting you on suspicion of illegally overstaying in the UK. You and your family will be prepared for immediate removal.' I feel like I'm watching a film where everything is happening to someone else.

That's when it happens. Dad turns to me with such a look of disappointment that I gasp. *Disappointment?* Why would Dad be disappointed in me? Then I see why. The heavy-duty security chain on the front door, bought to secure the door after the last Home Office raid, is dangling free and unused. I feel sick. My job was simple. Lock the door. Bitter saliva collects in my mouth. I need to swallow but my throat won't work. The Home Office got in because I didn't do my job. Out of nowhere, there's a roaring in my head and I'm punching and yelling, 'Get off my dad.'

Mum is distraught. 'Julienne. Stop. We behave like animals, that's how they will treat us.'

Out of the corner of my eye, I catch Beti's horrified face and the fight goes out of me. You can't beat authority with fists. You have to be smart. Use your wits. I relax my hands just as Jug Ears wallops me. I land badly winded and in pain, I don't move. Everyone freezes. He's an adult, I'm a kid.

Then Dad roars, 'I will have you arrested. I will make a complaint. You will not get away with this.' And Mum helps me up, crying her eyes out.

Knowing he was out of order, Jug Ears blusters, 'She attacked me. It was self-defence,' but he looks pale and is obviously freaked out.

Raincoat Woman tries to calm things down. 'Mrs Kizende, it doesn't have to be like this. Please. We need everyone to stay calm. Get all your paperwork – letters, documents, birth certificates – and we can leave quietly.'

Mum grabs the woman's hands. 'Why are you doing this? We are not criminals. They will kill us. The rebels will murder my husband, then come for my daughters—' The horror of what would happen next stops Mum in her tracks but Raincoat Woman nods as if she understands, her silver, shiny, peace symbol earrings swinging left to right.

'This must be a frightening time for you, but rest assured we wouldn't send you back if we didn't think you'd be safe.'

'My husband is a doctor. We were taken by the rebel leader to join his army. When we ran away, he vowed to bring my husband back in a box and feed him to the fish in Lake Tanganyika. Please, I beg you. Have some humanity.'

Raincoat Woman would like to argue but hours of training in How to Avoid Confrontation means she can only nod and tap Mum's arm. 'It's hard, I know, but at least you've got each other.'

Realising she'll never get through to her, Mum turns to me, whispering in French, 'You are my big girl, Julienne. I need you to be strong. Go get you and your sister ready. Take only the things you can carry.' But suddenly I'm not listening because I've just had the most brilliant, brilliant idea.

I am going to save us. Beti did it. Now it's my turn.

THE GOOD GIRL
IN THE ALL-TERRAIN BOOTS

CHRIS
RIDDELL

Hassan Abdulrazzak

THE GOOD GIRL IN THE ALL-TERRAIN BOOTS

What I am good at is reading body language. Had I been at the restaurant that lunchtime I reckon I would have read Karla's body language down to a T. I would have known she was nervous about meeting Hazem even though she was trying to hide it. Yeah, Hazem was her boyfriend. People are so cute with their 'boyfriends' and 'girlfriends'. Very adorable that long courting ritual they go through. Me, I make up my mind with one sniff.

Karla and I come from Mexico City. Hazem comes from a faraway place. He grew up in a city called Aleppo, in a country called Syria, in a region of the world called the Middle East. I used to watch the Discovery Channel at the base with my marine buddies so I've picked up a fair bit about world geography. Most of the marines laughed when they saw me watching TV. Not Hernandez. He knew I understood everything.

I found out afterwards that Karla met Hazem on that thing everyone is obsessed with: social media. Hazem always says he was trying to improve his Spanish and Karla says she was trying to improve her English. I don't believe them. I think they both liked the idea of flirting with someone from another territory, very different to their own. That's my theory.

War happened in Hazem's country. It was sudden and unexpected. I sort of understand war. I guess it's like when two packs fight over a turf. One side says this is my domain, I've pissed all over it, and the other side says no, it was I who pissed over it first. Then both sides jump at each other and begin snarling and biting. Come to think of it, you people don't do much biting, you prefer to blow things up instead.

When war broke out in Hazem's country, Karla was very worried. Hazem told her during one of their chat sessions that a sniper had shot at him as he was crossing a check point to get to university. Karla was fearful that next time Hazem wouldn't dodge the bullet. She wanted to bring him over to her turf, so to speak, where he would be safe. She helped Hazem get a place at her university in Mexico City. After years of chatting on the internet, they finally got to meet each other face to face. The first day they met, they kept yapping till the small hours of the morning.

Hazem started attending classes with Karla and everything went smoothly for a while; their love for one another grew day by day. Then a new group of Syrian students arrived. One girl, she began to flirt with Hazem. Karla was worried that he would prefer the girl from his own country to her. Karla had no idea what it must feel like being Hazem, having the ground beneath your feet open up, everything suddenly uncertain, having the label 'refugee' stuck to you forever, having to leave your patch of land and come over to another place with different people, a different culture, different food. She tried to imagine it but always failed. The way I fail when I try to imagine what a mobile phone would taste like. She wanted to lash out at the girl who was trying to steal her boyfriend but her heart wouldn't let her because that girl was also a refugee and she probably found solace in Hazem's company. If you ask me, Karla was too nice. If I had been in her shoes, I would have bitten that Syrian girl. Go and find your own boyfriend, I would have barked. But Karla isn't like me. She struggles to assert herself. Too nice, like I said.

*

Karla fidgeted with her knife and fork at the restaurant. *Why is Hazem so late?* she thought. If she had had a tail, she would have wagged it like crazy when she saw him walk through the lobby of the restaurant. She was always happy to see him. Hazem had a serious look on his face as he sat down. Karla's happiness turned to anguish. *That's it, he's going to break up with me*, she thought. Hazem reached into his pocket and pulled something out. It wasn't a treat exactly. Not the type I like anyway. But it was something you people value a lot. A box with an engagement ring inside. Karla covered her mouth in shock as her eyes lit up like those annoying lights you put up everywhere at Christmas.

The earth shook. Karla laughed and told Hazem she was going to tell their children how the day he proposed the earth had shaken. But then the earth shook again and again. The couple realised they were caught in an earthquake. Had I been in the restaurant with them I would have warned them long before the earth shook. I have a sense about these things. They would have fled the restaurant in time. On the other hand they might not have understood my warnings. You people can be stupid that way.

Everything suddenly collapsed. Karla and Hazem, the couple who had loved each other for years without seeing one another, the couple whom chance had brought together, were buried under rubble.

I was at the base when this happened. My trainer and partner Hernandez came rushing to my pen. He opened the door and said, 'Come on, Frida. We've got work to do.' He then knelt down and placed the blue neoprene, all-terrain boots on my feet and a harness over my body. I knew it was time for action.

We got into the van and sped towards the centre of Mexico City. I could smell the dust of the collapsed buildings miles before we arrived. This was a big earthquake and it had done a lot of damage. Was I up to the task? I was full of doubts.

I had been doing this work for years. Rescuing people. I am a Labrador. The usual breed of dog in my line of work is German Shepherd. I don't want to toot my own horn but I took to the training real quick. It was confusing at first when I started out. Hernandez would hide behind a tree or a bush and expect me to find him. Later he started hiding further away while another marine, Arauz, would make me smell a cloth with Hernandez's scent and shout a word at me. It sounded to me like 'Ho' at first. I had no idea what it meant. But as usual I followed my nose and it led me to Hernandez. This game was repeated over and over. Later, Hernandez gave me a cloth with some stranger's scent and shouted the weird word again. Now I realised the word wasn't 'Ho' but 'Go'. I figured out what I had to do. I followed with my nose the new scent and found a stranger, whom I'd never seen before, hiding behind a bush. When I found the stranger, Hernandez came rushing over and gave me a biscuit treat. He patted me down and said, 'Good girl!' I really liked it when he did that. I wondered when he goes home, does he give his wife a biscuit treat, pat her down and call her a 'good girl'? I'd like to think he doesn't. I'd like to think that was just our special thing.

I've been to cities all over Latin America, usually after an earthquake or other calamity had happened. Hernandez didn't need to give me a cloth to sniff. All he had to do was shout 'Go' and I would run searching for people in the rubble. I was so good at the job, I became a bit of a star.

That was a few years back. Now I was older and feared that my powers of smell were waning.

For the first time I was about to rescue people from my home town, Mexico City. This might be the most important day of my career.

The van stopped, the door opened and I jumped out. I saw another search dog with her trainer. Maya, the ferocious German Shepherd. She belongs to the Mexican army.

Our eyes locked. We wanted to growl at each other but our training prevented us from doing so. She was much younger than me, full of ambition, hungry for fame. I could see she was after my title. She wanted to be the top rescue dog.

Her army handler, Cortéz, looked at Hernandez as he patted Maya's back. 'Frida is getting a bit long in the tooth, isn't she? Maybe it's time she retired.'

Hernandez patted my back and stared right back at Cortéz. There is big rivalry between the army and the marines. The army people think they are better than us. All I can say is they can go sniff my butt.

I heard Hernandez say to Cortéz, 'I think there is still some juice left in the old girl.'

Old girl? Old girl? Oh dear Lord, even Hernandez thinks I am getting old.

He knelt down beside me and whispered, 'Frida, this is a bad one. We really need you.' He put the special goggles over my eyes and gave my behind a slap. 'Go,' he shouted.

I ran towards the building in front of me and began to climb the rubble. Hernandez was right behind, holding onto my harness. The all-terrain boots help but it is tricky work. You have to test the ground as you go along. You could easily step on a piece of concrete that cracks beneath you and fall right through. On the other hand, you have to hurry because time is of the essence on these rescue missions. Every minute that passes could reduce the chances of survival for those buried under the rubble.

I sniffed and sniffed but could smell nothing. I kept climbing the mound of rubble and sniffing. I began to panic. Usually I would get a hint of a human by now. According to the Discovery Channel we dogs are a thousand times better than humans at smelling things. With age, we lose the keenness of our smell, the way old humans lose the sharpness of their eyesight. From the top of the rubble I looked at the building next door. Maya had found a small child there. The army folks pulled the child out. The people of the neighbourhood helping the army clear the rubble began to clap and cheer very loudly. Cortéz patted Maya down and placed a treat in her mouth. I felt a pang of jealousy.

I heard Hernandez say, 'Come on, old girl, don't let me down,' as he followed behind me. There was a distinct huff in his voice. He too was getting old. I don't think the tacos his wife cooks for him help his waistline.

I kept climbing and sniffing. Nothing. They wouldn't have brought me to this building if they didn't think there were people trapped inside. I had to keep going. I took bigger and bigger gulps of air. I finally sniffed something.

It was coming from a hole in the concrete. I shoved my head through it. Hernandez tugged at my harness. 'Easy, girl.' He didn't want me to jump through the hole. Thank God for the goggles because a cloud of dust erupted in front of my face as I brushed the edge of the concrete. My eyes slowly adjusted to the darkness beneath me. Broken chairs, broken tables, broken plates, scattered food. I took a gulp of air and I could smell bodies. I started barking. I had an irrepressible urge to jump through the hole. I could feel Hernandez tugging at my harness with all his might. 'Wait! Wait!' He always did that when I was tempted to go under the concrete. I think he was worried that I would get injured. He pulled me back and shined his torchlight through the hole. 'Hello?' he shouted. We could see two or three bodies now. They were not moving. Sometimes we find bodies that are blue, cold to the touch and don't move. Hernandez always gets sad when he sees such bodies. And I get sad because he gets sad.

'I think they're all dead,' he told Arauz who was climbing the rubble behind us.

'Maybe we should keep moving,' said Arauz.

It was at this point that I heard a low moan. It was a female. It was so faint that only I heard it. Hernandez and Arauz were discussing whether to descend through the hole or move on to save time. I pushed my nose deep into the hole and took big gulps of air. I could sniff more and more of the female human's scent. She was alive; her scent told me so even though it was obscured by the smell of the dead and all the dust coming off the rubble.

'Hazem,' she cried out softly. Hernandez still couldn't hear her. It was then that I began to bark loudly. I shoved my nose through the hole, sniffed the scent, pulled my head out and barked again. Hernandez got it. 'There might be someone alive down there. We better take a look.'

Hernandez and a small rescue team began to widen the hole. They used a ladder to descend inside what had once been a restaurant. From the top of the hole I could see their torchlights go this way and that. Hernandez called for a stretcher. They placed someone on it and with the help of other marines pulled the stretcher out of the hole. That was the first time I laid eyes on Karla.

She was restless, moaning. 'Hazem, Hazem.' The name, unfamiliar to Mexicans, meant nothing to the rescue team. I worked that out because they didn't react to her moans and continued carrying her down the mound of rubble to safety. I, on the other hand, could read her body language down to a T even though she was delirious. I followed the rescue team to the ambulance. Hernandez came out of the hole and called me. 'Frida, come back.'

'Hazem!' Karla kept shouting but the ambulance crew assumed she was a foreigner uttering something incomprehensible. I jumped inside the ambulance and sniffed her dangling hand. I picked up the scent of Hazem.

It must have been the trace of his hand on hers when he put the engagement ring on her finger.

Armed with this new knowledge, I ran back up the pile of rubble, past Hernandez, through the hole and down the ladder.

'Frida, stop!' he shouted. Beneath me now was the marble floor of the restaurant. I could see blue, cold humans all around me.

'The concrete could collapse on you. Get out of there, girl!' shouted Hernandez.

He was right. I could feel a low rumble in the concrete. It was too dangerous to be here. Yet I knew from her body language that this 'Hazem' was very dear to Karla. She had uttered his name with all the sadness of a dog howling after its owner.

'Frida, come back!' Hernandez shouted at me through the hole. 'We looked down there. There is no one else alive.'

Maybe he was right but I couldn't let the matter go. I sniffed and sniffed. Damn it, if only I was as young as Maya, I could have picked up Hazem's scent so easily. My body was failing me.

'Frida, come back. Obey the order,' Hernandez said as he tapped on the ladder.

He was right, I concluded. There was nothing there. I began to head towards the ladder when, all of a sudden, I picked it up. The scent was so faint I might have imagined it.

'Frida, come back now!'

I didn't listen. Instead, I turned around and followed my nose through the shattered restaurant. It was so hard to move through the space because of the collapsed ceiling, cracked ground and broken furniture. I could feel the crunch of the smashed plates beneath my blue neoprene boots.

I saw him. Hazem. A huge piece of ceiling had landed on him and obscured him. His face was blue. He was not moving. I got close to him. I licked his dust-covered face.

No reaction. I brought my nose close to his nose to feel for the faintest sign of breath. I barked and barked and barked.

After the earthquake I became a bit of a celebrity. A Hollywood actor tweeted a video of me at work, adding, 'What did we do to deserve dogs?' and his tweet went viral. Many fans suggested that my face should be on the 500 peso note. I was paraded through the city and people came out to see me and cheered. Everyone took photos and videos of me and posted them online. It was all a bit hysterical if you ask me. I can't help but think that this social media you are all so obsessed with is the human version of a dog chasing its tail.

Several years later it was time for me to retire. I had finally lost the battle to Maya. Now she was the top dog. The plan had always been that Hernandez would adopt me when it was time for me to hang up my blue neoprene boots. Annoyingly, however, his wife had borne him a lot of children and there was no longer space in his house for me. I think she did it on purpose because she was jealous and didn't want to share her husband. If I wasn't so well trained, I would have gladly bitten off a chunk of her ass to teach her a lesson.

So there was a big question surrounding what would happen to me. There was even talk of putting me down.

One day, Hernandez opened the door of my pen and said, 'Frida, it is time.' I felt nervous because I'd never heard his voice sound so sad. I thought that maybe I was going to be sent to the vet surgery. Old dogs who are sent there never come back.

I followed Hernandez out into the courtyard of the marine base. I picked up a familiar scent. I looked up. It was Karla and beside her, in a wheelchair, was Hazem.

HASSAN ABDULRAZZAK

The couple had visited me several times after I had rescued them. They were often accompanied by TV crews. Hazem had lost his leg in the earthquake. The press were fascinated by how he had managed to endure the war in his homeland, survive the earthquake in Mexico, and experience the loss of his leg, and yet still find the will to complete his university degree, set up a business and marry Karla. 'I have the tenacity of Frida,' he would joke.

This time they were alone, not accompanied by any press. Karla knelt down and motioned for me to come to her. I ran into her arms and received a warm hug. Hazem motioned for me to leap into his lap and I did so. I pressed my nose to his and was glad to feel him breathing.

I now live with Karla and Hazem in their house in the suburbs. The experience of having survived the earthquake has brought the couple closer together. Karla no longer has to imagine what it would be like for the ground beneath her feet to open up all of a sudden. She has experienced that first hand.

Hernandez comes to visit every now and then (whenever his wife lets him). I sometimes miss the old days of rescuing people. I think Hazem is the only one who understands the loss I feel. Maybe because he lost his country then his leg. So on Sundays, he puts the old goggles on my face, the all-terrain boots on my feet and hides himself behind a tree or a garbage can and lets me find him. He then feeds me a biscuit treat and pats me, saying, 'Good girl.' I've never seen him do that with Karla. I don't mind telling you folks that makes me feel very special.

Recently I have detected a weird smell. It is made up of a bit of Karla and a bit of Hazem, but has a scent signature all of its own. It is hiding inside Karla. It can't hide forever. Sooner or later I will find it.

Moniza Alvi
EXILE

The old land swinging in her stomach,
she must get to know this language
better – key words, sound patterns,
word groups of fire and blood.

Try your classmates with
the English version of your name.
Maria. Try it.
Good afternoon. How are you?

I am fine. Your country –
you see it in a drop of water.
The last lesson they taught you there
was how to use a gun.

And now in stops and starts
you grow a second city in your head.
It is Christmas in this school.
Sarajevo is falling through

a forest of lit-up trees,
cards and decorations.
Mountains split with gunfire
swallow clouds, birds, sky.

EVERY DAY
IS CHRISTMAS...

Jon Walter

EVERY DAY IS CHRISTMAS...

We arrive on Christmas Island too late to see the crabs. It has been a week since the last of them passed on their way from the beach and by the time we are brought in through the gates, they have become invisible, lost in the shade of the palms and ferns that surround the camp.

'You have missed the crabs,' Enku tells my mother as she leads us to our bunk beds.

'What crabs?'

'The crabs that come every year.' My mother looks unimpressed. 'You will see. They turn the whole earth red.'

The camp is full of rooms that are either too large or too small. In the canteen where we have our meals, the voices of all those people make it difficult to hear the person sitting next to you, but in the room where we meet the man from the government, there is hardly any space for the four of us. He sits on one side of the desk and we are on the other. There is only one chair, which my father must use if he is to speak to the man with authority, so I stand beside my mother, the tip of my head reaching up to her shoulder. The man tells my father what happens now. How there are procedures that must be followed and the likely course of events. He says we will receive our letters directly, sketching out our future in stationery, the brown manila envelopes that will make their journey back and forth from here to the mainland.

My father has only one question: 'When?' He wants to know how long before this letter or that decision will arrive, but on each occasion the man can only hold up his hands, inviting us to judge the empty space between them. 'It will take time. One can never say how long.'

Before we took the boat, my father was a busy man. In Addis Ababa we had a calendar that hung on the wall, full of scribbled notes and coloured crosses that told him when he would be speaking in a hall or where the next rally would be held. He asks for one here and is given a photocopied sheet of paper for the coming month. It has a box for each day, but only large enough to make a mark. He puts a cross against the day we arrive and each day that we hear nothing he marks another until at the end of the month the boxes are full, each one the same as the other. He rips the paper from the wall in a fit of disgust.

'Do you know how the others mark their time here?' he asks me. I shake my head. 'By the number of times they have seen the crabs.' He crushes the paper in his hands and tosses it into the bin. 'Abel?' He waves me closer with a flick of his hand. 'You are twelve.'

'I know.'

'Soon you will be thirteen. What will be different?'

I don't know what I should say. No one knows the future. Perhaps nothing will have changed.

'Stand against the wall,' he tells me. 'Now, put your back straight. Don't slouch. And lift your chin up.' He puts his hand on my head, pressing firmly to flatten my hair, and then he makes a mark with his pen, a straight line of black on the wall near our beds. 'What is time?' he asks me. 'Is it always the same? I don't think so. Have you noticed how it's different here? It appears to move so slowly and yet the days mount up quickly. I am worried that I can't remember what I did the day before last. That's because time is only real to us if it is used meaningfully.' He points to the mark on the wall above my head. 'This is your height when we arrived. By the time you reach thirteen, you will be taller. We need to remember that.'

When I meet new people, in the canteen or out in the compound where we take our walks, I ask them how many times they have seen the crabs. Faraz has seen them only once, the very last time they made their migration, but he says he shares a room with a man who has seen them four times. 'Would you like to meet him?'

I go with him through the corridors and up to a dormitory where six men are lounging on their beds. He points out the man closest to the window. 'Rafiq? This is Abel. He wants to meet the one who has been here the longest.' He ushers me closer. 'Abel, this is Mr Rafiq Safi.'

I look at the four-crab man. I find it hard to tell whether he is young or old. He wears white cotton trousers and a shawl around his shoulders. A stack of brown envelopes sits on a small table beside his bed. He shakes me by the hand and takes a good long look at my face. 'How old are you?' he asks, sitting up straight and putting his feet down on the floor. I tell him I am twelve and he nods. 'The same age as my son, Tawas.' He points at two photos pinned to the wall near the head of his bed. One is of a woman and the other is a boy much younger than myself. 'They are still living in Afghanistan.' Mr Safi looks at my face then back to the photo, trying to compare the two of us, searching for the changes that will have occurred in the time he hasn't seen him.

'You can measure me if you like.' I put my back against the wall. 'Put your hand here.' I show Mr Safi the top of my head and when he has his hand in place I duck away from the wall and pin the photo of his son so it is at the right height. 'There,' I tell him. 'This is where it should be. That's how tall your son will be now.'

Mr Safi smiles. 'And my wife too? She stands this high.' He shows me with the flat of his hand against his chest and

I move the photo of the woman upward and then we both stand back, imagining the rest of them in the space of yellow wall beneath their heads.

Before I leave, Mr Safi puts his own back to the wall and asks me to mark his height too.

'Are you still growing?' I ask him, stretching up to make the mark.

'No,' he tells me. 'I'm afraid I may be shrinking.'

My father brings the first brown envelope back to our room and opens it solemnly as my mother and I watch. He takes the pages out carefully, making sure he doesn't crease them, and begins to read.

'Is it good news?' my mother asks when he lowers his hand.

'It is no news at all.' He offers the letter so she can read it for herself. 'They need more information to process our application. That is all.' The letter has a separate page with questions asking for dates and the names of people. It has taken four months to arrive.

My father finds a pen in the bag that we brought with us. 'I shall start on it after lunch.'

It seems to me the letter has great significance and no significance at all.

'Will you measure me again?'

Father makes me stand up straight with my heels together before he puts his hand on my head. 'That's strange. Have you been eating your food?'

'Yes.'

'That's good. But there's no change. You must be spending too much time thinking. You need to let the food get down to your legs.'

My mother brushes her fingers underneath my chin to tickle me. 'Never mind,' she tells me. 'We shall just have to wait.'

There is a clock on the wall of the canteen where I eat my meals. You can stare and stare but you will never see the hands move. The thing to do is to look away, to forget about it and then, when you look again, it will have changed. One minute. Five minutes. All of the hours between breakfast and supper. They always pass. It doesn't matter what you do. And I have become like a clock for my parents who watch my face for signs of change, hoping that out there in the real world, their case is moving forward, bringing their future towards them while they look away.

In Addis Ababa, as we were preparing to leave, my father told me many things about Australia. He made up stories for me, showed me pictures of kangaroos and hats hung with corks from all the bottles of beer you can drink in a day. Even on the boat, on the day we saw the shark, he told me stories of how beautiful the beaches are.

Mother says that stories fill you up with all the goodness in the world. That they help to make sense of who you are. But now all the stories they tell me are of their past. The time my father rode a camel to the university or the day he went to meet my mother's father for the first time and had to run from the dog that guards the house.

Another letter arrives. Another brown envelope. Their letter informs us that our papers have been lost, that the process is broken and we must begin again. There is a copy of the same questions my father answered two months before and which he must now answer again. I feel too ashamed to ask to be measured, but my mother remembers and it's good news. Enough to make her smile on a dismal day. I have grown. Sometime between the first letter and the last. A full two centimetres.

I rush across to Mr Safi. In his room the men are sitting close together and talking in loud, angry voices. Faraz is with them. 'We need a protest,' he says. 'Something that will make them listen to us.'

But Mr Safi shakes his head. 'Who will we protest to? There is no one here who doesn't already know.'

'Then we should do something, something so large that word of it will spread out into the world. Then they can't ignore us.'

'Gently,' Mr Safi tells him. 'Let's go gently!'

Faraz shrugs. 'It's up to you, but you will be watching the crabs again this year unless we do something.'

Mr Safi sees me waiting. 'Do you have some news for me?'

I step into the ring of men. 'Yes, I do. I'm two centimetres taller.'

I put my back against the wall and he makes a new mark with his pen. We move the picture of his son higher up the wall. 'Do you want me to measure you too?'

'No need,' he tells me smiling. 'I feel taller already.'

Today is unlike every other day. Something is happening. From our window we can see people moving out into the compound. Some are leaning up against the perimeter fence with their fingers curled around the thin metal tubes. My father looks anxious but he takes us outside, my mother and myself, the three of us holding each other's hands for reassurance. And we hear them immediately, the tick, tick, tick of a million claws clicking on the hard road, making the sound of every second we have spent here. Each crab is bigger than my father's hand and there are so many of them, too many to fit the width of the road. They are pushing themselves up against the perimeter fence. The quicker ones are climbing over the backs of the slower. And they are bright red. An endless river of red that picks its way along the stretch of road then turns into the last line of trees between us and the beach.

My father watches them for a long time. 'What a strange country this is, where they put people behind fences and let their animals run free.' We follow the fence till it reaches the gate. 'Everything here is upside down.'

And then I think of Mr Safi. I go back along the fence, trying to spot him in the long line of people but he isn't here. I go back inside, into the dormitory where he stays, and there are the men, all of them watching him stand at the window.

'Mr Safi!' I run over to his side. 'Mr Safi! The crabs are here!'

From the window you can see the dark green forest, the shade cut through with thin red lines. And Mr Safi's mouth looks similar, the dental floss stained red against the dark skin, where he has sewn his lips shut.

'Oh, Mr Safi! What have you done?'

Faraz puts a hand on my shoulder. 'Sometimes silence speaks the loudest. Now they will listen.'

When I tell my father about Mr Safi, he nods as though he already knows. Or perhaps because he understands. He reaches out and puts a finger to my lips. 'Enough now.' He leans forward, looking at me closely. 'See here? You are getting a moustache. Have a look in the mirror when you next use the bathroom. You will soon be a man.' He is pleased with me. 'Have I ever told you the story of when I first began to shave?' He looks back over his shoulder, to make sure we are alone. 'It involves a girl. From the time before I knew your mother. I thought she was the most beautiful girl in all the world.'

And he begins another story, to pass the time while we wait.

Since 2014, the detention camp on Christmas Island has been scaled down, with refugees being moved to new, larger camps on the islands of Manus and Nauru. As with the UK, those seeking asylum in Australia can be held in detention indefinitely.

#owned

Fiona Dunbar
#OWNED

Kal sat on the balcony, thinking about pants. Well, it wasn't exactly a balcony, and he wasn't sitting on it, as there was nothing to sit on. He was by the balcony. The non-balcony. The rusted steel frame that used to be a balcony, before the concrete part had fallen away. Basically all there was now was a hole in the house – the 'squat', as it was called. And this squat was his new home.

He was waiting for the van. Everyone was. The van brought supplies from the huge donation centre on the edge of town. Nappies, tinned food, clothes.

Kal really needed pants. Don't get your hopes up, Yaz had said. But pants were a big deal when you had no spares and the ones you were wearing gave you a sweaty wedgie that was hard to ignore. Used to be, Mama would order them online by the dozen: big bags of perfect cotton underwear with confident elastic. Flying pants, winging their way to him via the magic of the internet. And it really did seem like magic now. Here, internet and phone signals were like mythical creatures, more talked about than existing. Not that either of them were much use to him any more, since he'd lost his phone.

Someone had told Kal that when you're stabbed in the gut, it feels like a punch. But thinking about home, and Mama... it all hurt so much more than a punch in the gut. Proper stabbing pains. Nausea, too. He just had to block it out, so he let his mind wander to flying pants instead. Doodling in his tiny notepad, he drew pairs of Y-fronts with wings: whole flocks of them, soaring over the city. It almost made him want to laugh. Almost. He'd collected the dregs of the last batch of clothing: things no one had any use for. A solitary shoe. A handbag. A gigantic, misshapen T-shirt. Kal was good at life hacks, but even he struggled to think of a use for the first two. He'd keep the T-shirt, though. It occurred to him that he could turn it into two or three pairs of underwear – if he had some elastic. Not much use without elastic. Still, he could use it as a towel.

A horn honked down in the street. Kal peered out, hoping to see the van. It had to get here soon, surely. Yaz and the others had headed out to the donation centre first thing that morning.

Nope, still no van.

Just a guy and a girl standing there, staring at the squat. Tourists.

Kal knew what he was meant to do: disappear inside. Don't be seen, don't engage. And don't be photographed. You could be turned into a pulsating dot on a map, like a bullseye on a target. You don't risk all, only for that to happen. Kal knew all this, but he was exhausted. And in a defiant mood. He wanted to stay out here, watching for the van. They should be shamed into leaving.

The girl wore a white jumpsuit, a tiny backpack and a collection of bands on her wrist. Head down, she stood a short distance away from the guy, who gawped up at Kal through mirrored sunglasses. His pink shirt was tucked into knee-length shorts, and he wore brown leather shoes with no socks. Kal thought this was odd, as he certainly looked like someone who could afford socks.

The guy just went right on staring. Then he held up his phone.

Kal felt the rage rise inside him. Why? he thought. What

was he to this guy? Something like a caged creature in a zoo? What?

Still he fought the urge to hide away. Maybe he could win a staring competition here. Yeah. That would be a cool superpower to have, a killer stare, only without actual killing, just a small electric shock, maybe. A little zap.

He'd have liked to zap that woman with the hairdo earlier that morning. She'd asked where that smell was coming from. Kal hadn't understood. What smell? The whole city stank. Then someone explained that the woman assumed he and his kind did their poos in the street. By the time Kal had taken this in, the woman had moved on. It was too late for a zapping, or even so much as a bit of caustic cussing. Not worth it, they'd said. Save your energy. You'll need it for when the ones with the firebombs come. And they will.

The guy and girl were still there. The girl dangled around awkwardly while the guy fiddled with his phone. Had he taken pictures? If so, what would he do with them? Kal began to regret not hiding away after all. He felt a strange mix of loathing and panic.

Then the girl turned and gazed directly at him. Looked him straight in the eye. Kal stared back. Please delete them for me, his stare said. Delete, delete… A lump formed in his throat. Finally, he found his voice and called out, 'Can I help you?'

The guy didn't even look up from his phone. 'No, we're good, thanks!' he called back.

Zap! Zap! Kal's stare zoomed in on the shiny black phone, willing it to slip out of the hands of Mr GOOD-THANKS, and into the gutter. Preferably down the drain.

If only.

Never mind, here at last came the van.

Kal prayed for pants…

*

'It's a bit like the Wild West round here, you get me?' said JJ, as he steered Ana up the hill.

'How do you mean?' said Ana.

'I mean, wild. No police, it's lawless.'

JJ grinned at her, shining red face, gleaming teeth. Two bulbous-headed, nervous Anas stared back at her in his mirrored sunglasses. She paused, rubbing her calf with her foot.

'Oh, but you're safe with me, sweetcheeks!' said JJ. 'Hey look, there's one. See?' He pointed. 'That's where they live, in there.'

The place was a wreck. So many broken buildings round here, all sprazzled with loud, angry paint. Ana felt as if she'd passed through an invisible looking glass into some sort of grimy Death Metal version of the city they'd left behind.

'C'mon, babes, I wanna get nearer.'

'Yeah... it's the bites.'

The mosquito bites really were bugging her. JJ had slapped one against the wall last night with his Timberland deck shoe: fat red splodge.

JJ tugged her along. Ana swallowed her anxiety. She hardly knew him, really – something her mother had thrummed into her endlessly. Two months, not long enough... Well, she was grown up now; it was her life. And JJ was interesting to listen to. He was well travelled, knew so much about things she'd never experienced. Sailing, stuff like that. When he kissed her, it always came as a surprise, because she'd forget that she was there too.

'Oh, cool!' said JJ. He whipped out his jet-black iPhone and pointed it at the house.

Ana saw that a boy was sitting in one of the windows, looking out. She wondered how she'd feel if she were him, being stared at – being photographed, even. She turned her gaze to the ground, let her hair fall in front of her face. She wished she could just push the door behind her and be back on the other side of the looking glass. 'JJ, I'm not sure...'

JJ held up one finger, put it to his lips – sshh! He went right ahead and took the pictures.

Ana rubbed at her bites with her sandal. Glimpsing from behind her curtain of hair, she saw that the boy in the window was staring back at them now. He was about her age, she thought. Not bad-looking, despite the shabby clothes. Slender yet well toned. Agitated, though. Even at this distance, she felt that. Not surprising. Why was JJ doing this? What was taking him so long?

JJ flipped through the images till he found the one he liked best. His thumbs worked furiously as he loaded it to his Instagram, then fiddled with the image, getting it just how he liked it.

'JJ,' Ana tried again.

'Yeah, just a sec,' said JJ. 'I forgot to add...'

Ana waited as he put in another hashtag. He already had half a screen's worth of hashtags. Lots of hashtags meant maximum likes, and JJ took great pride in collecting likes.

Ana wandered off a little but lost her nerve and circled back. Then she hated herself for doing so, because she knew she was doing it out of fear. Still she felt the boy's gaze. Finally she let go. She looked directly back at him. Not staring, not gawping, but surrendering. She wanted to be like a sponge: mop up the grief, the resentment, the pain. She knew he must feel those things. It wasn't the sort of thing that JJ talked about, but those stories were always in the news: the terrible journeys, the drownings, the borders with electric fences and tear gas. Throw it all at me, she thought. I can take it.

Still JJ stood there, fiddling with his phone. 'Gah! It's not sending. No fricking signal in this dump.'

'Can I help you?' the boy called out.

JJ raised his arm, still staring at his phone. 'No, we're

good, thanks!'

He went on staring at his phone as he moved on up the street.

He didn't see the van coming.

'JJ!' cried Ana, reaching out…

Yaz was sweating now. She'd never driven a huge van like this before. She hadn't been completely honest about that, but the driver hadn't shown up, and people needed things that couldn't wait. Yaz needed things that couldn't wait – ones she couldn't bring herself to ask for. And her little cousin needed nappies. And there was that boy who just arrived yesterday – Kal. He'd reminded her five times about the underwear.

'I know,' she'd said. 'It's the same for everyone.' She didn't add, you think you've got problems. Try staunching a steady flow of blood for a week. Try keeping a baby clean on one nappy a day. No, that wouldn't be helpful. Something terrible had happened to Kal. Terrible things had happened to all of them, but the rumours she'd heard about Kal were hard to believe. She wanted to be able to help him in some small way.

Here it came again, the searing pain, radiating from her belly. Breathe, breathe. The pain was bad enough, without the added stress of trying to steer a thumping great metal can through calamitous streets, with a pair of guides too busy chattering half the time to remember to give directions. And all the honking, and the bikers and pedestrians coming out of nowhere. Gears that crunched and stalled, and a steering wheel that was on the wrong side. And wave after wave of pain.

But now they were out on the open road. Straight line. Just keep going. And breathe.

At the donation centre, selected garments were on display. A ski suit. A bizarre pair of crimson platform boots.

Why those things? Yaz supposed they were decorative, but also spectacularly non-useful. She made a beeline for the pharmacy section. Nappies: yes! They even had the right size for her little cousin. Just as Yaz braced herself to ask for the other things, another cramp came. It was so powerful that it was all she could do to stop herself from doubling over. 'And, uh... adult ones...' Her voice was faint. She could see the packs from here, but had to wait to be handed them; that was the rule. It didn't matter that she could barely speak, though, the woman knew. She pressed a single pack into Yaz's hands with an apologetic look. 'This is all we can spare,' she said.

Wrong size. Never mind. Yaz thanked her and ran to the ladies' room. She'd started to leak, never mind. Thank heaven for black clothing. Thank heaven for adult nappies, meant for old people with malfunctioning waterworks. No sanitary towel could do the job so well, for so long. Not even the ones with wings; those adhesive flaps that attached to your underwear. If you had any. Thank heaven for baggy clothing.

Almost delirious with relief, Yaz caught up with the others in the clothing section and helped look for things. She moozled in the fustious pile of clothes; no amount of washing could quite restore them to freshness. Other lives hung in them still: lives of people who were maybe dead, or bored, or never-liked-that-shirt-anyway. People with armpits and cigarettes, aftershave and skin disease. Soon she was half-buried in the soft, shifting mound, breast-stroking her way through it. She hoped to find a few things that weren't transparent frimlies, cardboard tent-dresses or pinstriped Enormitrousers.

Finally, she came up for air. She folded everything neatly into plastic bags. Some people would be disappointed, she knew. There was an orange T-shirt with a picture of a surfer and the words SURFIN' CALIFORNIA on it. She held it up for the others to see. 'How about this, for Kal?' she said. 'It's got his name on it, look: KAL-ifornia!'

'Ha!' They humoured her over the lame joke. It wasn't really funny at all. But maybe Kal would like it, just the same. It wouldn't make up for the no-pants situation, but it was something.

They loaded the van. Some useful odds and ends were thrown in at the last minute: shower gel, Band-Aids, a roll of thick elastic. She climbed up onto the blistering hot seat and braced herself for the return journey, her head now pounding as well. She hadn't had enough water.

The city traffic had reached boiling point. The one-ways were different in this direction, and her hot, hungry companions kept making mistakes. Finally they yelled HERE HERE – LEFT! and Yaz hit the squealing brakes. She made the turn. Phew, home stretch. The glare off the greasy road made her squint as they rolled down the hill to the squat.

WATCH OUT!

Yaz slammed on the brakes. Someone had just wandered into the street, right in front of her. She hit the brake harder, but now it felt as if they were on ice. Wheels squealed, rubber burned...

When Kal reached the street, the air was sliced through with brake-screams, and the girl cried out something like 'JAY-JAY!' Tourist Guy stumbled, the van slid and screeched. Kal ran up the pavement towards it... Tourist Guy lurched between two parked cars, and out of his hand flew the glossy black phone, glinting in the sunlight as it turned somersaults in the air. The van juddered to a standstill diagonally across the street, a fraction of a metre behind him.

It seemed Yaz had been driving. She looked shaken as she stepped down and rushed to see if the guy was OK. Others spilled into the street. Someone went to Yaz's aid and defended her against Tourist Guy, who was completely unhurt but lashing out, swearing his face off at her. Someone else climbed into the driver's seat; another motioned to oncoming traffic to back off...

Kal started towards Yaz, then felt a hand on his shoulder. He turned. It was Tourist Girl. Dewy upper lip, wide eyes, breathless. She pressed something to his chest and spoke, but it was hard to hear over all the commotion.

He blinked at her.

'Oh-eight-oh-one,' she repeated. 'It's the passcode. Take it. Quick!'

Kal glanced down at the glossy black rectangular thing in her hand, then back at the still-raging Tourist Guy.

'Go on!' said the girl. 'I'll smash it anyway if you don't take it.'

Kal clamped his hand on it. Still silky-smooth, not a crack in it. He slid it into his pocket. She was gone before he could find the words to thank her: running down the street, tiny backpack bouncing.

Oh-eight-oh-one, he repeated in his head. Oh-eight-oh-one...

SANA
THE
REFEREE

CHRIS
RIDDELL

Peter Kalu

SANA THE REFEREE

With the water about to turn turbid, Sana stirred the saucepan water again. Clouds became small bubbles breaking free from the saucepan base in a charge upwards. Enough. She spooned the eggs quickly, one after the other onto the plate, which she then carried across the kitchen. She joined the end of the line. They all stood back. Marco, the Il Palagio Head Breakfast Chef, began his assessments.

Words sprayed from Marco's lips in English, Italian and French, occasionally with a clatter of cutlery as he dropped the tasting fork on a plate.

'Too hard!'

'Too soft!'

'Raw!'

'Bad shape!'

'Shredded!'

She didn't understand why they were doing this competition, and why four servers had been allowed into the kitchens to cook with them. Il Palagio was frequented by prime ministers, diplomats, football stars and celebrities. To get the job she'd griddled eighteen cheese-on-toast samples at interview. The chef had rejected fourteen and still she had been best of her group. They paid her the minimum wage for nineteen-year-olds, out of which she had to pay to have her whites laundered every day, then came the agency's cut. She brushed away these thoughts. Marco's voice drew closer.

'Fluffed!'

'Merged!'

'Ruined!'

She didn't know on her first day at work whether she was appalled or terrified by the profligacy that occurred in the quest for perfection – the sheer waste of eggs, cheese, bread, meat. And she had been lost in the Babel of the kitchen's languages – Arabic, Farsi, Congolese French, Ethiopian, Italian, Polish, all mingling with varieties of English. Everyone yelling. Cursing. The impossible speed they worked at. Gradually, for no reason she could understand since she had done no course and it was mostly new to her (for instance, eggs were never poached in Kurdish cooking), she rose. When she stuck out a hand and called for a pan, immediately it landed in her palm: 'Here, Chef.' She rescued others' dishes sometimes, showed them quickly the correct level of flame, how to beat, when to stir.

Marco was mid-line:

'Stringy!'

'My God, hopeless!'

Lunchtime was close. The entire diplomatic corps of the Italian Embassy often visited for *cucina casalinga*. The servers had to at least be able to speak the menu properly. Sana was happier backstage. Tips were pooled between kitchen and servers after the management took their cut. On a good tips week, she sent money home. She had dreamed she would complete her degree in International Relations then be sitting with those diplomats, examining maps, solving the world's problems. Her father had called her My Little Diplomat because of her knack for breaking up fights in the family, ending feuds, coaxing a smile from tears.

Yet here she was cooking eggs.

Marco's voice drew closer. The Head Breakfast Chef's

glee in scorning their efforts shone brightly above his rumbles of derision.

'Leaking!'

'Fallen apart!'

'Abysmal!'

'Kiss my dead mother, who did this?'

Marco was in front of her.

'Me, chef.'

'Egg four's yolk is damaged, you let it sink too low, but the plate is beautiful. Winner is this plate!'

The chef spun away.

'Kitchen monkeys, you were not as awful as last year. Server clowns, dreadful – best stay out of the kitchen till next year!'

Everyone laughed. Marco swept out of the kitchen, the four shamed servers trailing behind him like runny eggs.

Sana received a handshake or two. Little hugs. The honour of the kitchen staff had been maintained. Any acknowledgement of their worth was a welcome fillip, useful when the curses from the maître d' rained down on them. She felt a glow inside. This absurd life.

Julie broke her reverie. 'It means you're the referee, Sunday.'

'I don't understand.'

'Every year, Kitchen plays a football match against Servers.'

'Seriously?'

'On a proper pitch with goal posts and everything. The best poached egger is made referee. Don't ask why. The match is played on a Sunday, in pouring rain, and always ends with Marco being awarded a penalty and scoring the winning goal.'

Julie leaned her face close into Sana's and lowered her voice to a whisper: 'To avoid fights, referees should not accept bribes or invitations to have sex, or unusually generous shift arrangements in the days leading up to the match.'

Julie laughed at Sana's shock and squeezed her shoulder. 'You'll be OK.'

The lunchtime craziness broke out. Yelling. Banging. Invectives.

Over the next four days staff quizzed Sana. She proved her mettle. Having grown up with five football-mad brothers, she comfortably despatched questions on the off-side rule, the distance players must stand from the ball upon free kicks and which was the greatest team in the world (Soran City FC, followed distantly by FC Barcelona).

In Soran, she'd watched the big matches at home in between power cuts and surfing the internet for scholarship opportunities. That surfing had eventually landed her at Stirling University, UK. Stirling's temperature had been like someone left the air con dial on max all day; you might as well stand under a waterfall. Here in London, at least the weather was milder. She imagined her cousin Dahat and her mother in the AC'd guest room, wondering where beautiful Sana was, what was she doing, why had she not phoned? Only in these moments would Sana lose her mind, forget where she was, who she was, why she was, whether ON was to turn the cooker dial to the left or the right.

'Drink this. Your blood sugar's low.' Julie again.

Football in Soran was where she developed her powers of persuasion.

'Why do I have to come in? The match is nearly finished and we're twelve goals and they are sixteen, but they are tiring. Please, sister. One minute more.'

'The ice water is melting. We've taken it out of the freezer.'

'Now? Right now?'

'Yes, little brother.'

'With watermelon?'

A nod.

'I'm coming.'

The lunch shift was done. Sana caught the early bus, alighted one stop before and waded through the Hounslow throng where planes roared so close you could almost see the people sitting in the seats. There was a hotel called Sacha's near the stop. Its first door was for happy-hour drinkers, the second for hotel rooms, the third where they sold old sports clothes by weight. She spotted what she wanted and was in and out quickly.

Arriving at her house, Niroke giggled when she showed her. It was a nylon tracksuit, the inner lining grey, the outside black. In the house, only Niroke had a mirror. Some of the other house occupants were best avoided anyway – their borrowings or rememberings or paying backs rode their conversation like daemons and hijacked a simple request for a stick of sugar into a flow of laments, expletives, Home Office letter interpretations and some bastard boyfriend with his stupid sperm.

Niroke was sitting cross-legged on her bed with a cup in one hand and a wide scowl on her face. She had a great range of scowls as befitted someone whose life was a medley of Royal Appointments: Earl's Court, Government House, Royal Appeal Tribunal, Her Majesty's Constabulary. This particular scowl of Niroke's was accompanied by a slight peeking of her tongue, making it her Fashion Diva thumbs-down face.

'Is it that bad?' Sana quizzed. She turned to the wardrobe mirror and looked. Her thighs were not too large, her bottom was well concealed if she tugged the zippered jacket down a little more and her breasts were hardly noticeable since the top was extra-large.

Niroke spat some water out onto the mini-rug that covered the floorboards. 'Run up and down,' she commanded and indicated with her arms. Sana tried this and immediately Niroke slid off the bed with laughter. The two of them did some running on the spot, referee arm waving and pretend whistle blowing. Later they went downstairs and cooked together.

The sound of the toilet flushing woke Sana. She found herself on Niroke's chair, the tiny television blaring. Niroke was on the bed, her mouth agape, her body a floorboard. Sana unplugged the television, turned off the room light, slipped the catch of Niroke's room door as quietly as she could, pulled it shut and padded to her own room. She closed her own door then silently sobbed.

The Sunday came. Sana rose early, pulled on the tracksuit and visited an old friend she'd lost touch with. She ate breakfast with her then walked with her and her child to the toddler park nearby. Her friend talked of everything except family but Sana didn't press it. Just as her friend didn't press Sana on why the government had forced the cancellation of her scholarship and ordered her to return home to explain her political articles. They sat on the swings watching her little boy play for a while before Sana made her excuses. They hugged in the Kurdish way. She walked back to the tube station.

The football pitch was a windswept field between two construction projects. There were no changing rooms. She hid her eyes as some of the players pulled on their kit. The Servers were playing in red-and-white hoops. Kitchen was in blue.

Sana called the two captains over and told them she expected them to listen to her whistle. They had to agree to this and only after would she toss the coin. The Head Waiter and the Head Breakfast Chef muttered their consent. Sana blew and the match got underway. The rain hosed the players and the wind tugged at their shirts but they played enthusiastically.

Sana raced up and down. Early on, they surprised her, following her rulings of free kick, goal kick or throw-in without dissent. She began enjoying the game. She decided many of them were no longer in the condition they imagined themselves to be in and that made her lenient when their lack of fitness caused clumsy tackles or inept collisions. They were grown men but their squabbles on the pitch were no different to those of the Soran street kids and they played similarly – hunting the ball in packs, yelling for the ball when they were in no position to control it, pushing and shoving during corner kicks, streaks of petulance, sly shirt pulling, occasional chivalry, and here and there a flash of brilliance.

Midway through the second half, the bigger-bellied ones were strolling and waving their arms more than pushing their legs. Opposing players galloped past them. The sly foulers abandoned slyness and tried brazen cheating. Her whistle heated up.

Inevitably it happened. She disallowed a Kitchen goal for offside. Kitchen formed a ring of jabbing fingers around her, accusing her of being a traitor, of having slept with assorted Server people, of having taken bribes. Servers jabbed at Kitchen's backs in Sana's defence.

She blew her whistle loud enough to frighten them all back, then shouted her explanation:

'When there is no opposing player between the attacking player and the keeper then where that player is interfering in play by impeding the goalkeeper's performance of his role, that player shall be deemed offside whether he receives the ball or not!'

There was a silence. Had she overstepped the mark? It was one thing to referee a match of her kid brothers, another thing entirely to boss these big men. Yet even as her mind hesitated, her mouth propelled on:

'These are the rules. Any more dissent and I will show the red card. Get me the captain who wants it. It's here in my pocket, cooked and ready to serve. Who wants it? Who's feeling red?'

The players backed away and Sana saw a new expression on their faces as they glanced at her in their retreat – a confused admiration that was uncertain of the phenomenon it was admiring but was sufficiently intimidated not to want to test its nature: a combination of *Who is she?* and *Who does she think she is?*

Sana laughed to herself because suddenly she didn't care. It was hardly fingerprint time at Secret Police HQ, it was a game of *footy*.

Five minutes before the final whistle, the Head Breakfast Chef duly fell over in the Server penalty area. As a dive, it was less dying swan, more drowning buffalo. Marco hauled himself to his feet, covered in mud and protest, the ball resolutely in his hands. He turned to her. As inevitably as the rise of the sun, he wanted his penalty. Sana blew the whistle.

LOCKED UP

CHRIS
RIDDELL

Michael Morpurgo
LOCKED UP

Aman

I thought it was Uncle Mir at first. Only a few days before we'd had a pipe that burst in our flat, and the water had flooded down through the floor into their place. I thought it must have happened again. So I got out of bed to open the door.

But it wasn't our door, and it wasn't Uncle Mir. The knocking was coming from downstairs, from the street door.

So I went down to open it. It was men in uniform, policemen some of them were, or immigration officers maybe – I didn't know – but lots of them, ten, maybe twelve.

They pushed past me and charged up the stairs. Then one of them had me by the arm and was dragging me upstairs. I found Mother sitting up in her bed. I could see she was finding it hard to breathe, and that any minute she'd be having one of her panic attacks. A policewoman was telling her to get dressed, but she couldn't move.

When I asked what was going on, they just told me to shut up. Then they were shouting at Mother, telling her we had five minutes to get ready, that we were illegal asylum seekers, that they were going to take us to a detention centre, and then we'd be going back to Afghanistan. That was when I suddenly became more angry than frightened. I shouted back at them. I told them that we'd been living here six years, that it was our home. I told them to get out.

Then they got really mad. One of them pushed me out of Mother's room and back into my bedroom, and told me to get dressed.

They never left us alone after that.

They wouldn't even go while we were getting dressed – Mother said afterwards that there were at least three of them in her room all of the time, one of them a man. They hardly let us take anything with us – one small rucksack and my schoolbag, that's all.

Almost all of our stuff got left behind, my mobile, all my football programmes, my reading books, my David Beckham autograph. Ahmed's little red engine, and my goldfish.

But I had my silver-star badge in my jeans pocket, so at least I didn't leave that behind. They never stopped hassling us. They took us down the stairs and out into the street. There were lots of people out there in their dressing gowns, watching us – Uncle Mir, and Matt and Flat Stanley too. Matt called out to me, asked me what was going on, and I told him that they were sending us back to Afghanistan.

A policeman had me by the arm the whole time, pushing me, frogmarching me. It made me feel ashamed, and I had nothing to be ashamed about. Mother was having a proper fit by now, but they didn't bother. The policewoman said she was just pretending, putting it on.

They shoved us in this van, locked us up in separate compartments, with bars on the windows, and then drove us off. I could hear Mother crying the whole time. They must have been able to hear too, but it was just a job to them. They were busy listening to their radio, and laughing.

I kept talking to Mother, trying to calm her down, but I could tell she was just getting worse. I banged on the door and screamed at the police in the front, and in the end they did stop. They had a look at Mother, and the same policewoman told me again that she was play-acting, and to shut my mouth or I'd be in trouble. I didn't keep my mouth shut.

I told them I wanted to be in with Mother, and kept on and on until they let me. Mother calmed down a bit after that, but she was still in a really bad state when we got here.

They wanted Mother and me to be in different rooms. They said I was too old to be in with her. I told them I was staying with her, to look after her, no matter what, that I'd been with her all my life, and there was no way we were going to be parted. We said we'd both go on hunger strike if they did that. We made such a fuss and noise about it that in the end they let us stay together. That was when we learned not to give in, not ever.

When I first came into this place, I couldn't believe it. I mean, it might look all right from the outside, like a recreation centre, a bit like my school. But inside it's all locked doors and guards. It's all a fake, just to make it look good – fake flowers on the table, pretty pictures on the walls, a nursery, places the kids can play, and television. But it's a prison. That's what it is, a prison. That's what I couldn't believe. They put us in a prison. We were locked up. I hadn't done anything wrong, nor had Mother, nor has anyone else in here. Everyone's got a right to ask for asylum, to try to find a safe place to live, haven't they? That's all we've done.

For the first few days in here, Mother just cried and cried. Uncle Mir came to visit, and he said he'd get the lawyer and he'd do all he could to get us out of here and back home. But nothing could stop Mother from crying. When we heard the news that Uncle Mir had had a heart attack, and was in hospital – on account of everything that had gone on, I suppose – it only made it worse for her. The doctor came and gave her an injection, and after that, instead of crying, she just lay there looking at the ceiling, as if she'd got no feelings left inside her.

It's worse for her than it is for me. She's got her memories, of the prison they took her to back in Afghanistan. I know they're terrible memories because she still won't talk about them. She says she's never ever going back to Afghanistan, that she'd rather kill herself. And I know she means it too.

That's almost it, the whole story – oh yes, except for one thing. About a week ago, I think it was. They came into our room one morning early, and told us they were going to take us to the airport, and then fly us back to Afghanistan. We asked them when it was going to happen, and they told us it was right now, and we had to get ready.

We refused.

Mother fought them, so did I. They had to hold us down and handcuff us. And in the van all the way to the airport we hammered on the side of the van, and we shouted and we screamed. They drove us right to the plane and tried to make us walk up the steps. We wouldn't go. They had to half-drag, half-carry us up. Even in her seat on the plane Mother wouldn't stop fighting them. I had almost given up by then, but Mother never did. That's why we are still here, because Mother didn't give up.

In the end, the pilot came along and said he couldn't take off with Mother and me on board, that we were a danger to the other passengers, that we were frightening them. So they took us off the plane and brought us here. They weren't at all pleased to see us. Our wrists hurt where they'd handcuffed us, and were a bit bruised all over, but we didn't mind. Mother told me that night that Grandfather would have been proud of us. He had been a fighter for freedom, and so had Father, in his own way. We must fight for our freedom, and never give in.

Lucy Popescu

INTERVIEW WITH JUDITH KERR

'If one has spent one's childhood as a refugee in a
succession of strange countries, one's family feels like an
island separate from the rest of the world...'

Judith Kerr was born in Berlin in 1923 but escaped from
Hitler's Germany with her parents and brother in 1933
when she was nine years old. Her father was a drama critic
and distinguished writer whose books were burned by the
Nazis because he dared to speak out against the regime.
The day after the family left Berlin, the authorities came
to arrest them, and throughout the war there was a price
on her father's head. Judith and her family passed through
Switzerland and France before finally arriving in England
in 1936. Judith wrote about her experiences in her classic
autobiographical story, *When Hitler Stole Pink Rabbit*,
which – along with *Bombs on Aunt Dainty* and *A Small
Person Far Away* – forms part of the *Out of the Hitler Time*
trilogy.

She won a scholarship to the Central School of Arts
in 1945, and since then has worked as an artist, television
scriptwriter and, for the past fifty years, as an author and
illustrator of children's books. She married screenwriter
Nigel Kneale in 1954 and they had two children together.
The Tiger Who Came to Tea was Judith's first picture book

and was published in 1968. She wrote it after telling the story at bedtime to her daughter Tacy and son Matthew (Matthew went on to become a writer himself, winning the Whitbread Book Award for *The English Passengers*). The book has become a classic and appeared in the *Telegraph*'s list of top children's books of all time. It has sold over 5 million copies and is still going strong.

She is also renowned for her feline creation, Mog. This enduringly popular character has charmed generations of children and has starred in a whole stream of books. In 2015 Mog took to the screen in a major Christmas advertising campaign, highlighting the importance of sharing at Christmas. The accompanying book, *Mog's Christmas Calamity*, shot to the top of the bestseller list and helped raise vital funds for Save the Children to improve child literacy across the UK. The year 2015 also saw the publication of *Mister Cleghorn's Seal*, Judith's first fiction title since 1978. Inspired by a true story about her father, Alfred Kerr, *Mister Cleghorn's Seal* tells the life-affirming tale of Mr Cleghorn who, on a visit to the seaside, rescues a seal pup named Charlie. Her most recent picture book, *Katinka's Tail*, was published in October 2017.

Judith lives in south-west London. In 2012 she was awarded an OBE for services to children's literature and in 2016 she was awarded the BookTrust Lifetime Achievement Award. She has no plans to retire, saying, 'I'm miserable if I'm not working. I hope I never have to retire and I count my blessings that I'm still active.'

Lucy Popescu: What was your earliest reading memory?
Judith Kerr: I remember my father and mother reading to me and my brother when we lived in Berlin.

LP: When did you first decide you wanted to write?
JK: I never wanted to be a writer. I'm much more of a

drawer, an illustrator. My earliest memory is from when I was two. I remember sitting on the kerb and we were all playing in the street, and there was a patch of petrol that had spilled on the street. I was stirring it with a stick to make all the colours move about, and the other children kept calling me to come and play. I remember thinking for a moment and deciding that stirring the petrol was more important.

LP: Do you follow a particular routine when you are writing/illustrating?
JK: I work every day if I can. After breakfast I will go up to my studio at the top of the house. The only good thing about being on one's own is that I can work twenty-four hours a day if I want. If I didn't work, life wouldn't have a shape, and having all this time I have got better. I start about half past ten, eleven. Sometimes I can go on until six. In the evening, I go for a walk along the Thames for about an hour. It helps me to think. If you have a problem with work, hopefully you get towards solving it with walking. When I get home, I often have a whisky.

LP: Why did you decide to write about your experience as a refugee in three books? What, if anything, did you hope to achieve?
JK: I remember going to see *The Sound of Music* with the family, and Matthew, my son, came out and said, 'Now we know what it was like for Mummy when she was a girl.' So I wanted to tell my children about my own childhood, what it was really like. My husband Tom was a great writer and brilliant at construction. He told me that I needed to put Hitler on the first page. I managed to get Hitler on the second page. I wasn't sure how to do it but Tom gave me a lot of advice. I didn't want to write it in the first person as you have to be 100 per cent accurate to do that, I think.

LP: Did your art and writing help you process your experiences as a refugee? And how, if at all, did your early experiences help shape your later work?
JK: I don't think so. The experience of being a refugee was so different for me. I never saw anything bad. Although my parents' lives were destroyed by it, my brother and I always agreed that the childhood we had was infinitely better than the one we would have had if we had stayed in Germany. We loved living in different places and learning the languages.

LP: What has made you the writer you are? Why do you think you have endured as a much-loved writer and illustrator, touching and delighting readers across generations?
JK: It must be something to do with my great age. I've been doing it for so long that some of it must be OK. I have been very lucky too in having the same publisher for fifty years.

LP: When you were young, what did you miss most from your native Germany?
JK: I suppose I missed my friends but we loved the change, the different places that we lived and learning the language. I don't miss anything about Germany and I don't have any family there now, but I have been back to Berlin several times. Most recently I went with my grandchildren and we went to see the house where we lived.

LP: Because you were a refugee you had to learn three languages: German, French, English. What is it like losing/gaining a language?
JK: I loved learning new languages and particularly French, which was wonderful in its brevity after the long German sentences.

LP: When you first arrived what did you love most about England? And now?

JK: People were so kind to us during the war. Even though we were German and my parents spoke very little English, we never witnessed any unkindness. There was an official name for Germans who were classed as enemy aliens, but people like us were officially called 'friendly enemy aliens' because we were German but also known to be anti-Hitler. We had to report to the police if we went more than five miles away, so we knew the police well and they were so kind. My father once said that if he left England he would have to take the whole population with him. England is my home. I owe this country so much.

Eoin Colfer
CHRISTOPHER

Marco dreamed of lying in fat green grass and gazing at blue sky. Sometimes the dream was so solid in his mind that he thought it must have actually happened. In another life maybe.

A thrown spool of thread knocked his forehead.

'You dreaming about grass again?'

Christopher. Of course. The Kenyan boy's smile was white in his dark face.

'Grass? Grass like fat worms?'

'Caterpillars, stupido,' corrected Marco.

Christopher frowned. '*Cat hair peelers?* You are stupido, Marco baby.'

Marco chuckled twice. It took a lot to drag two chuckles out of a person in this place but Christopher could do it.

'You are the stupido, Christopher *baby*. And you stink like the backside of a sick dog.'

Now Christopher chuckled. 'Backside of a sick dog. This is a prince among insults.'

Heavy footsteps creaked on the floorboards and the boys stopped their joking. Bluto was on the workfloor. The factory foreman honked into his phone for a minute then hung up, muttering about whatever new problem the phone call had brought him. This was a dangerous time. Bluto fined people when he was upset.

Marco hunched low into his work, shutting out the

universe. This was what Bluto wanted to see in his employees: *a good work ethic.*

On this Sunday Marco was stitching gold wings on the pockets of fake Nike shorts. The wing was the adopted symbol of the AC Milan striker Costas Andioni.

'Andioni breaks his leg and we're gonna be picking these wings out with our teeth,' Christopher had whispered just loudly enough for everyone to hear, earning himself a clout on the ear and yet another visit to the office.

Mrs M had left the door open so the workers could hear what happened to smartmouths.

'This ain't no sweatshop, Kenya,' she had shouted, her shrill voice rising to the concrete ceiling. 'You're free to go anytime you want. You want to go, please go. You going, Kenya?'

Christopher shook his head, chin so low it touched his chest.

They have broken him, thought Marco. *Even brave, shining Christopher.*

But when Christopher returned to his bench, the first thing he did was to ask whether Marco had farted.

Not broken. Still Christopher.

Marco never offered backchat as he could not afford to be docked an hour's pay. Bluto loved to dock wages. Christopher said that whatever Bluto took from you, he kept for himself to buy rare Pokémon cards for his collection. Everyone pulled their weight at Marco's home; even the twins helped to make the foil roses that Mother sold at the city's traffic lights.

'Speedy, Mister Bluto,' Marco would say, hating the man even as he smiled. 'Just the way you like it.'

And so he worked that day. Wing after wing. Gold thread on the inside, red flames feathered around the border. Marco worked without a break until dusk, until his backbone was a glowing rod and his fingers were claws.

Eventually, he leaned back and sighed, his breath pluming like chimney smoke. Mrs M always turned off the heat around midday, claiming that the workers' own industry should keep them warm.

Marco pushed back his chair, tugged at his cushion to make sure it was tied down securely, then walked stiffly towards the bathroom past the thirty or so workers.

In spite of the factory's chill, a dense smell clogged the building. There was bleach in the mix, and sweat, rubber and oil. Though he knew it was merely a soup of chemicals, Marco imagined the smell was alive. He could use this in one of his stories.

Marco often wrote stories, most featuring Quantum Boy (Marco himself) and his sidekick Dreadlock (Christopher, of course). Quantum Boy zipped through time, getting himself entangled in famous historical adventures, and Dreadlock was always on hand with a witty comment at the right time. For example: *This time you have come up short, Napoleon.*

Marco ducked quickly inside the cramped bathroom. He did not pull the bulb cord because then Mister Bluto would see the light leaking out under the door and come to hurry him along.

The bathroom was colder than the rest of the building because it wasn't really part of the building. There was a gap one block wide all the way around where the breeze blocks had subsided from the factory proper. The wind whistled through and froze the toilet seat.

And while Marco warmed the seat with his palm, he did not notice the click-clack of Bluto's approaching footsteps. And because there was no light on the floor, Bluto presumed the bathroom was empty.

The supervisor barrelled into the cramped space backwards, shouting at his phone.

'I said Tropical Mega Battle, gold edition, you idiot. Not bronze. I won't pay a penny for bronze.'

Bluto did not realise Marco was there until he sat on him. Even then he did not know that it was Marco, because if he had he surely would not have run onto the workfloor with his trousers in his hand, screaming: 'Toilet monster! It bit me. They are real. I knew it. I knew it.'

The experience was not pleasant for Marco either. One second his life did not seem to be in any immediate danger, and the next there was a sudden overpowering smell of sweat and cheese and his face was mashed by back fat.

Marco stumbled into the factory, squinting and gasping like a prisoner released from his dungeon.

'Sorry,' he coughed, knowing that whatever had happened would be his fault. 'I'm sorry, sir. I must hurry back to work.'

Bluto lurched forward, grabbing Marco's shoulder.

'Tell them, boy. You must have felt it.' Then Bluto stuttered to a halt as the truth became clear. It had been Marco in the bathroom with the lights off. Only Marco.

'No toilet monster,' he breathed, calming himself with gulps of air. 'Just a boy.'

And for a moment he was happy, then the red tint of embarrassment coloured his cheeks. By now every worker in the factory had gathered round; even Mrs M had come from her office to check on the disturbance. She stood, wrapped in her knee-length puffa jacket, glaring at the foreman.

'When I was a child,' explained Bluto, 'my brother told me stories of a monster who lived in the toilet bowl.'

It was ridiculous, even to his own ears.

'This boy!' he shouted, hoisting his trousers with one hand. 'Skulking in the bathroom with the light off. He must be docked! Fired!'

Christopher piped up from the throng of workers. 'The toilet monster. He is the one who must be fired.'

A few workers tittered but not Bluto. 'Shut your mouth, Kenya. This boy must go.'

'But if Marco goes, who will stitch Andioni's wings?' asked Christopher. 'The toilet monster? His fingers are clumsy and he will drip on the material.'

More laughter now, even Mrs M's mouth was twitching at one corner.

'Please, Mrs M,' pleaded Bluto. 'Fire him now.'

Christopher contorted his face and limbs in a hilarious impression of a dull monster trying to sew.

'Arrrrrgh. Dis work be berry difficult for poor toilet monster.'

Bluto dropped Marco and charged at Christopher. The other workers clapped and whooped as Christopher easily dodged the foreman, weaving between the machines. The fun might have lasted for longer, had Mrs M not anticipated Christopher's route and snagged him by the ear as he shot around a corner.

'That's the end of your little game, Kenya,' she snapped. 'Into the office with you.'

Bluto was still in attack mode, but Mrs M froze him with a single pointed finger.

'And you! Prepare my peppermint tea. And in future, whistle before entering the bathroom. Everyone knows that the toilet monster cannot bear whistling.'

'A good joke, Mrs M,' said Christopher, still smiling.

Mrs M shrank his smile with another tug on the ear, dragging the skinny boy towards her office where he would surely be fired.

Marco did not know what to do. Quantum Boy would blast Mrs M into the dinosaur age, but Marco had no special powers. He was a scared boy who still hadn't used the toilet. Though he felt a little guilty, Marco backed into the bathroom, remembering to switch on the light. In the corner of his eye something moved. It was Mrs M. Her office window could be clearly seen through the gap between the bathroom and factory wall.

Before Marco realised what he was doing, his arm was through the gap, seeming to pull the rest of him after it.

It was a tight squeeze, but Marco sucked in his ribcage, flattened his nose and managed to inch through the gap until he emerged into the factory yard. The sky was wrong. Where there should be the dark blue of night, there were orange-bellied clouds, reflecting the city's streetlights.

Go back, whispered Marco's good sense. *Go back.*

But he did not.

The window blinds were old and missing several slats so Marco's view was barely obstructed. He made a funnel with his hands and looked through it to the room inside.

Mrs M was behind her desk shouting at Christopher, who sat in a wooden chair facing her. She shouted and pounded the desk, making the pens jump.

I must call out to him, thought Marco. *Share the blame. Perhaps Mrs M would fine us both and fire neither.*

But then Marco noticed that something was not right. Mrs M smiled and even winked at Christopher, who did not seem in the least afraid. As a matter of fact he seemed comfortable and relaxed, propping his knees on the desk and helping himself to some peanuts from a bowl.

Marco moved further along to a spot where the pane was cracked and a dagger-shaped sliver of glass had fallen out.

'Another incident like this and you will be let go, Kenya!' he heard Mrs M say.

'Thank you, Madam,' Christopher said, his white teeth like rows of chewing gum. 'I will be a good worker.'

It was all fake, Marco realised. For the benefit of those listening on the factory floor.

Mrs M spoke again, this time in quiet tones. 'You go too far with Bluto,' she said. 'Your job is to keep the workers happy. Happy workers are hard workers.'

'Bluto was scaring Marco,' said Christopher. 'He is the best one we have.'

Mrs M was impressed by such wisdom. 'You are right, dear Christopher. If Marco had gone, ten more would follow him and the Andioni order would never be finished on time.' She opened her desk drawer and took out a few notes. 'A small bonus for my Trojan horse.'

Christopher took the money and tucked it into his sock. 'You should tell Bluto to leave Marco alone. He is soft but I like him.'

'I will tell him. Now, you go back to work.'

'Five more minutes, a can of Pepsi?'

Mrs M smiled almost tenderly. 'One can. Five minutes, then you go out of here crying like a baby.'

Christopher pushed out his bottom lip.

'No one cries like Christopher,' he said. Then in a typical Christopher motion he popped out of the chair like a circus acrobat and trotted across to a small fridge on the floor. He selected a cola and stretched on the ground to drink it.

'Drink slowly,' Mrs M chided. 'Or you will give yourself a tummy ache.'

Christopher's reply was a gentle burp.

Marco turned away from the window. His friend's job was safe, that much was clear. But was his friend his friend?

Dreadlock is gone, he realised. *There is only Quantum Boy now.*

Marco felt cold and betrayed. Christopher had been masquerading as their comedian, when all the time he was under Mrs M's wing.

Even so, I still laughed. Does it matter why he jokes?

It did matter, Marco decided. Christopher's jokes were like glossy red apples with black sludge at their core. He would not laugh again.

Marco felt sick to his stomach and wished that he could just go home. But he knew he must return to the factory.

Before he went back inside, Marco allowed himself one last longing look at the lights and life of the city beyond. His mother was out there somewhere, selling foil roses at the traffic lights of east London.

Brian Conaghan
HAVE YOU SEEN ME?

I mean, I'm no a racist, but...

Have you seen them with their buggies
On buses,
Dodging fare,
Clamming up when applicable,
Urging their children to beseech,
No interest in integration,
Assimilation?

Have you seen them?

Now, I'm no a racist, but...

Have you seen them get everything that's going?
Benefits for this, that or the other:
Unemployed,
Refugee,
Asylum-seeking single fuckin' mother
Pilfering our Social Welfare
School system and free health care.

Have you seen them?

Come on, I'm no a racist, but...

Have you seen them get all our houses
for their hordes of brothers, sisters
and spouses?
Babies born on our NHS debt
Automatic citizenship
For this tinted, tainted set

Have you seen them?

Honestly, I'm no a racist, but...

Have you seen those cadgers with kids on their back?
Not tricking me.
There's plenty's in their sack
Always under attack, no wonder.
I mean,
They could have some English coming out their gobs
Before they dilute our culture
and blag our jobs.

Have you seen them?

I wouldn't say this aloud, but

If they can't make it here
With the culturally convivial
The great receiver
Flag in hand
Inebriated welcomes

A quid or two
Then I fear
But, it ain't me...

I'm no to blame
For all this vacuous, bigoted shame
It's they, them and those
You should expose.
Ach...
At the end of the day it's just a bit of craic,
Not everyone wants to send them back
To...

Where is it again?

Which I'm ecstatic about as
I stand here a migrant, an exile
Just the same
Sans the nationality
Brood on back or linguistic disability.
But seeker just the same.
However, I'm nobody's menace
I'm received
I speak local tongue
And my skin blends me in.

You keep telling me you're no a racist, but,

Have you seen me?

AMIR AND
GEORGE

CHRIS RIDDELL

Sita Brahmachari
AMIR AND GEORGE

Road is moving too fast.

Mr Shaw he drive high speed to Speech Day final school.

Far I go from Kabir and Mirsa, from petrol smell of city, out from shadows of tower blocks. Only fields are here. More birds, no people. It is too quiet. Looks like Mr Shaw and me have moved to new land.

Look out of the window, Amir, I say myself. Look out!

Where there is houses in village, windows show Christmas tree lights shining and I feel little better. But everything I am watching from outside. Like last week in class we watch *Christmas Carol* by Charles Dickens, when this boy is looking at happiness through the window. This is my first Christmas here. I still feeling on outside of window looking in. But I am not tiny boy, like this Tim. People think I am tall and strong-looking, like man. Kabir says to me, 'Stop growing, Amir. Your head is already more high over mine!' My father was tall man, not like Kabir.

Mr Shaw is feeling in festival spirit. He sings with radio some words: 'Weather outside is frightening...' But he smiles at same time, relaxing in driving.

'Why it is frightening?' I ask.

'What's frightening?'

'The weather... in song.'

'No, not frightening, Amir... Frightful... It means bad weather!'

'So why are they happy to be with bad weather?'

Mr Shaw laughs. 'The lyric's about feeling warm and comfortable in your house while the weather is cold outside.'

It is warm in the car, but I am cold. Now I am thinking it is my fault how I come in this situation. I am for blame alone. I see this question for public speaking competition outside Mr Shaw's office. I sign my name on list. I say to my friend Mo, 'You enter with me.' But he say, 'This is not for us. They will make fools from us.' Now I wish I listen to him.

'Have you been out of the city before?' Mr Shaw asks me.

'No, never.'

'You've come a long way, Amir, in just one year!'

I think long, long way and this is long, long road.

'What do you make of the countryside?'

'I don't know it.'

'I'm a country boy myself. You can take the country out of the boy, Amir, but you can't take the boy out of the country.'

'This is true! You will never take my country out from me,' I tell Mr Shaw.

He looks at me then back to motorway. 'I'm sure that's right, Amir.'

Mr Shaw is looking like he's young man, not wearing his worrying lines across forehead like he wears in school. But I am opposite. My heart is not light, not comfortable. It fires in my chest like shelling.

'Mr Shaw, I change my idea. I cannot give public speech at final.'

Mr Shaw stops the radio. 'But Amir... You persuaded me that you should do it. I wasn't sure, but you've proved me wrong. You've done so well to get this far. Don't give up now. Anyway, you've given that speech so many times – you know it off by heart.'

'Yes, confidence is OK in the city... not in this country.'

'But Amir, this is the same country. It's just the country*side*, that's all.'

'For you maybe so. You feel more in home here, I feel better in city.'

My mind runs slow with many new pictures after we drive from the city. Too many new pictures, too much thinking – like computer when many windows are keep open. Memory is full. I am in fear I will forget my speech, forget how to speak in English. Strength in mind is leaking from me.

We leave motorway road and now car is driving on long road with sheep on one side, sheep on other. Very slowly car is judder-judder over metal.

'Bloody cattle grids!' Mr Shaw is swearing. 'Sorry, excuse my language! The school's not far now, should be just around the corner.'

Now my mouth is open like eating air. Speech Final school is in front like grey castle. We walk on stone path. Not so long past, I walked from forest on path like this, with broken shoes.

'Shiny shoes, Amir!'

'Kabir polished them ready and Mirsa bought this new shirt. She says old school shirt is looking grey not white. I don't know.'

'They did well. You look smart!'

'They are wanting to come here today. For supporting me. I told Kabir it is not permitted. So he tells me – Amir, I will shine these shoes, then, when you look on them, you must think Kabir's confidence thoughts.'

Reception is big hall with tall stairs winding round and round. I look up to the top at paintings with gold frames showing people with expression to painter saying, 'I am very important person – VIP.' Giant faces staring on me from paintings. One woman with closed tight lips and white hair, wearing blue coat. I can hear this lady's sharp voice in my head – says, 'Go home, Amir Karoon. You do not belong here.'

Steps are wide and made in wood, not like concrete stairs of my school. In this landing here is painting of tall man wearing same blue coat. I ask Mr Shaw why all wear same blue dress coat and flat black cap.

'Graduation gowns and mortarboards,' he explains. 'You'll wear one of those one day, Amir – when you finish university!'

I don't know.

At top of stairs there is other painting. This man is not wearing gown and black hat. He is different-looking. Black hair, moustache... not so sharp. He is looking little piece like my father, how I remember him. Expression like his eyes are holding burning questions.

'The man himself – George Orwell – the reason we're here! Come on, Amir. Let's do this thing.'

Mr Shaw's arm is round my shoulder, walking me inside this hall.

So many hundreds students. Voices echo up to top seats, like screech of sea birds.

There is one Christmas tree with sparkle lights, this is most giant inside tree I ever seen.

'What a tree! You can smell the needles in the air.'

Often Mr Shaw he tells things I don't know what it means, but I don't ask every time. It makes me feel like small child knowing nothing. Needles in the air?

'Smell this pine, Amir!' Mr Shaw he takes some green spike from the tree, squeezes juice in fingers and gives to me. I test how sharp.

'Smells fresh, like sleeping in forest,' I tell him.

Then he looks to me, like he sometimes looks to me. Not funny now, like he is worrying.

Hall is coming quiet. Announcer Lady with hair in tight knot and black suit comes in stage. She says welcome to finals of George Orwell National Writing and Public Speaking Competition. She says we are all winning. I don't know why she says this. If so, why is it competition? Why do we come here? She asks all Final people to walk to stage and sit in seats. I stand like robot. I hear Mr Shaw say, 'I am proud of you, Amir Karoon.'

I don't want him to think I chicken so I walk to the front. I have no thoughts in mind. I have walk like this before – when I did not know which direction I will turn.

Announcer Lady gives me number card. I am seven. There are ten finalists, always ten. In past I like this number ten – not any more. The girl behind me, number six, she looks like Mikah how she would grow... if she would grow.

Now Announcer Lady is saying we are lucky to have important judges. She says announcement of names and each panel person stands and students is clapping. There is writer, politician, history professor and actor. When actor stands... I think I have seen in TV, but I don't know. She smiles, bows and all the people in this hall cheer and clap, stamping feet.

Announcer Lady welcomes first speaker to stage to address question for George Orwell competition: 'If Liberty means anything at all, it is the right to tell people what they don't want to hear.'

Number one is standing. Shoulders are wide. Even more wide from mine. His voice is like posh person. If you take film and say this boy is Prime Minister in five years' time, I believe you. He is saying about what is means by 'equality in society'. His speech is smooth, clear, easy. Then next speaker comes. Thing in every speech is strong statistics, numbers, repeating language. I don't know half of words. There is much I cannot understand. Number four boy is using all good technique, speaking in confidence, but his eyes stay like ice.

Now it is girl next to me. She is talking of racism. This I understand, but she takes different direction. She is giving interesting facts of racism in wide society, things she is saying I have not been thinking about before... like asking why so little diversity people are going to university. She is saying also about young black men in prison and how many cannot read. I did not know this. It is strange in such rich country, people cannot read. I really did not know these things. Now she is telling of gangs and why should people want to join. What is motivation? She is even doing some rap music, getting people to rap and clap with her. She is not copying format how to speak. She is someone who has her heart on fire.

I look to Mr Shaw. I shake my head like to say warning, *I can't do this.* He only smiles at me. My speech is like different species. My speech is only my story. Number six girl is finishing now and every person is clapping. The actor lady is standing and cheering. I think this girl must be winning. I hope she is.

'Thank you, Grace!' Announcer Lady tries to make people stop clapping. They don't want to. Now she must shout over clapping, using her hands to make audience quiet.

Number six girl called Grace tells, 'Your turn.' I don't know why I think her eyes are looking so like Mikah.

'Amir Karoon.' Announcer Lady is calling my name. 'Amir Karoon.'

Looking at my shoes, my legs are shaking. Now I am happy Kabir is not here to see me fail. My friend Mo will think I am fool. He will say, 'Yes, I told you it will be shame for us this way.'

'Amir Karoon.'

Grace is saying to me, 'That's you, isn't it?'

I want to say Grace, *I don't know what is me in this place.*

I stand. I have no notes like others. But I like to try to get things right, perfect like I can, so I learn this speech in heart... by heart. So my speech is better than the way I speak English. I speak like a script I learn of my story, mistakes taken out... most of time. In trials people like my speech, even if English is not perfect. People are voting to support me... maybe not only me, but also feeling about refugee children I am representing. I do this not only for me. This I tell myself, trying to build some confidence.

I am looking for place in hall to focus. I choose the star at high point of Christmas tree and I start to speak. But my voice is weak. Mr Shaw is smiling too much. Christmas light is shining on my eyes. I am thinking where is this tree come from? Maybe even the forest I hide in.

Each speech I start in same way. I remember the words I write in my heart and I start to speak. Mr Shaw tells me, 'Imagine words like a river flowing.'

I am Amir Karoon. This is my story. When I heard of George Orwell competition, I went to my teacher Mr Shaw and I observe to him... my English is not so good, but I can tell you something about this subject: 'If Liberty means anything at all, it is the right to tell people what they don't want to hear.'

I am speaking, but audience is looking one to other like something is wrong. Actor Lady is looking down at table, shaking head like she will cry. People move around in seats, whispering.

Mr Shaw is standing, making others move in row, excuse me, excuse me. Walking through hall. Now he is taking me by shoulder.

Announcer Lady is saying, 'There will be a short interval. Please remain seated – we will recommence in a few minutes.'

People starting talking. I can hear in their voices they pay me pity. I am sad loser boy they will go home and talk... I am foreign boy they will say... He is nothing, should not be making speech with so little English.

Mr Shaw takes me to room with one mirror, chair and soft sofa seat. He says it is a dressing room for theatre performance. I don't care what is.

Mr Shaw is wearing deep lines. 'What happened up there, Amir?'

'I was telling my speech like all the other times.'

Mr Shaw is shaking his head. 'Amir, I'm so sorry. You froze when you stood up there. I should have gone with my instinct. I should never have put you through this.'

'I know these words by my heart! I want to smash my stupid head.'

'Don't be so hard on yourself, Amir. You won't be the first or the last to get stage fright! Let me go and speak to the judges and see what happens now.' He is biting lips like he is not sure what to do.

Mr Shaw opens the door wide. I hear clapping. 'They must have started again... Amir, I'll be back in a minute.'

Words are in my head like waves moving in and out... Frightful, stage fright, frightening, fear, fear... Fear made me silent Boy again, made me suck on bitter lemon half. I am looking at my face in a mirror. Lights on border make my grey eyes shine.

My eyes grow bigger. In reflection I see other face. Behind in soft chair is sitting tall man, black hair, small glasses, wool jacket, moustache. Question in eyes. He smiles at me.

I don't know to turn or no, so I stay looking in the mirror.

'You're George Orwell, from the painting in hall?' I say to reflection.

'I am. And who are you?'

'Amir Karoon.'

'So tell me, Amir Karoon. What did you come here to say?'

'You looking little like my father,' I tell him. I begin to turn to talk with him.

'Amir, don't turn around. Please let me hear your story.' Reflection George takes a book from his pocket and a pen.

'What are you writing in your book?'

'Meeting with Amir Karoon... Old habits!' He smiles at

me. I don't get this, but I feel in my heart he is a good man like Kabir, like Mr Shaw. 'Take your time.'

I sit tall and take deep breaths. Then I look him in his reflection face.

*

I am Amir Karoon. This is my story. When I heard of George Orwell competition, I went to my teacher Mr Shaw and I observe to him... my English is not so good, but I can tell you something about this subject: 'If Liberty means anything at all, it is the right to tell people what they don't want to hear.'

*

'I like that title,' Reflection George says, leans forward in his chair. 'Go on!'

*

This is not the country I am born in. My land is Iraq. I came here one year ago, when I was thirteen years old. Now I am fourteen. When I come... came here, I had little English. When I came here I had not much speech at all. My speaking voice I think was buried in war... ash and dirt. You see I was looking for my mother, my father, my brother Suli, under fallen wall of my garden. I find... I found nothing but one lemon. I put it in my pocket. I think how it is... how is it—

*

'Don't worry! It is, is it – just speak, Amir!' Reflection George says.

*

How is it possible I can find this lemon and not my parents? Days I look for them. I am hungry. I am thirsty. I can't find water, so I bite the lemon in half. Bitter taste is in my mouth, like in my heart.

I look down on my feet and they are walking. Like they know better than me, I must leave to survive. In my mouth I hold the lemon half. My face is swollen like fish shape. I suck in bitter taste, I walk, I cry, I taste the bitter, I walk, I cry. I follow others. I do not know where we go, but it is somewhere. Only one thing I know is we walk away from my home, my land.

Sometime people talk to me at border... at checkpoint. I have no papers. One soldier he ask me, where do you go?

I stay silent.

He asks me, 'How old you are?'

I do not answer.

Then he pays me pity. 'Go through, go through, son. Try to join another family. You must walk three days to get to camp for refugees. Inshallah you are strong boy, you will be safe.'

I think maybe camp can be a better place for me.

This is the moment I must step away and be Boy. If I stay Amir, I cannot speak this part of the story. This is the moment where I ask you to switch off pictures you see on news, step sideways out of your everyday mind, like when doors slide from real world into dreams.

Boy is walking.

*

'And that boy is you. Isn't it, Amir?' Reflection George says.

I nod. I turn to see if he is real.

'Don't turn back now, Amir... Go on!' he says.

*

Boy is walking. A strange boy who sucks a lemon in his mouth.

What is he walking away from?

Death.

What is he walking towards?

Life.

Boy will ask each one of you if you will do the same in his shoes. He thinks you will.

Boy is in search of a sweet taste. He can tell you this. If you eat too much poison it takes long, long time to feel sweet again.

Camp is not the home Boy hopes for. Camp is many people. Many, many people who want only to be home. Camp is a dangerous place for this silent boy.

Boy sees many things. Many people here have poison flowing in their blood. Poison makes them ill, like good meat when flies suck too long in heat.

One night into his tent walks a man of rock. Boy calls him Rock Heart.

He says Boy must go with him. He says he takes children to freedom. He says, 'You must not speak. You must be silent.'

He does not know Boy has lemon-half in mouth. Only if he spits it, he can speak, and Boy has no wish to speak. Rock Heart takes Boy's hands and pulls him out of tent. Boy starts new life, but this man does not care to give Boy a name.

In that night, in that darkness, Rock Heart takes five boys, five girls from camp. On many days' walking, Rock Heart is not kind. He is not gentle. He is not good. Boy does not like the way he looks at girls, especially Mikah from Boy's village. Rock Heart has wanting eyes like grown man should not look to young girl. Boy holds Mikah's hand to keep her safe. Rock Heart man spits on Boy. 'What are you, fish face? Her great protector?'

'Hurry, hurry,' he say. 'We must reach the sea for dawn breaking.'

Boy is afraid of sea. He cannot swim.

Rock Heart pushes Boy inside the boat. Boat is not good-looking. Boat is soft like toy you take for holiday.

'Look after this lot! Valuable cargo if you can get them to the other side!' Rock Heart tells Cargo Man. Boy sees they are passing money one to other. Cargo Man touches Mikah's hair. Making of her beauty a joke. She is starting to cry. Boy knows no one cares for them – all the children know this. Only Cargo Man is wearing jacket for saving his life.

Boy makes decision. If he gets to land in safety, he will run from Cargo Man. He will take Mikah with him somewhere no one may find them. Boy knows Cargo Man does not think to make them free. Poison blood... corruption like disease is spreading.

Sea is quiet in first hours. Moon is like a silver coin. Sea and sky are no difference – where one ends, other begins. Only land is missing. Stars is our universe shining. Boy wishes on light of universe to take him to safe place, Inshallah.

> *Boy is on the boat*
> *Sun rise, slow, pink, orange*
> *Red scar dawn*
> *Stomach heaves into Boy's mouth*
> *Sick is in the boat*
> *Stink is bitter*
> *Boy sucks on bitter. It is nothing new*
> *Best time of day is the time of two lights*
> *Twilight*
> *Where moon and sun kiss*
> *Then the sky is full of magic colours*
> *Anything can happen*
> *In his mind Boy sings to Mikah every night they live*
>   *on boat*
> *Sea stays calm for one whole night, then comes the*
>   *anger storm*
> *Boy is sure all must die*
> *Sun sets like giant, blood-red eye.*

Cargo Man's eyes are full from fear. He shouts for children to still. He stands. But children don't stop screaming. Maybe sea hears them cry. Wave rises up like justice hand from bottom of sea, reaches into boat and takes only Cargo Man.

Children are silent, holding for life on to rings on side of boat. Children are all hating Cargo Man... but now he is not here to hate.

Boy lies on the floor of boat. Sea is calm but sun is cooking skin. Lips are dry. Mikah sleeps on Boy's knee. Boy watches the waves. Mikah's head is a ball of fire. She is the sun.

Boy falls deep in sleep. In his dream Boy reaches land, takes Mikah's hand and runs away.

It is twilight when sun and moon kiss, but now it is too late for the sun. Boy takes lemon half from mouth and kisses Mikah's head. She is cold, but still he holds her. How many days must they rock like this together? Dead girl, living boy. Boy sleeps, he wakes, he sleeps, he wakes. There is no water, no more dreams of happiness. Boy closes eyes and prays to Allah for what is his will. He sleeps again and when he wakes there is land in the distance... Rescue boat comes to find... one boat with ten children. Only three are living.

Boy will not let Mikah go. Rescue people pull her from him and he screams like a wolf in the night. Then he puts the lemon in his mouth and sucks.

They take Boy to another kind of camp – with high wire walls. But before the wire, Boy escapes and runs and runs and runs into the forest. He lies on earth floor, face in dirt, and cries. He hears others in the wood. He is thinking, I am dreaming. He does not know how long he stays like this.

A woman's hands are on his shoulders turning him, speaking in his tongue. 'Is that you, Amir? Are you alone?'

This woman speaks Boy's name. It is Mirsa from Boy's village and Kabir. Friends of his parents. Mirsa takes the lemon from his mouth and gives him water.

They have baby Kalila... a daughter maybe six months old, but they hold Boy like he is their own son. They cry to hear Boy's story. They sing and pray for all the leaving and the lost. They eat what they find in the wood – berries and mushrooms. Slowly, slowly, Boy starts to hear his name. Slowly, slowly, he becomes Amir again.

Kabir has a plan. They say they have family in England and I should go with them. There are people who will come to help, but until this time, everywhere we go we must hide. We must not be seen.

Happy times and hungry times were in the forests. Mirsa singing to baby Kalila and me singing too. After singing one day, Mirsa tells me that if we go to England she will make me like her son. Then she will have one son, one daughter.

I keep the lemon in my pocket.

After the forest I take fever in my head. I cannot remember all this journey. Mirsa says it is good to not remember everything. It is mercy.

My body aches like I am bruise from monster lorry journey. We are like chickens packed inside on way to new camp they call jungle.

A jungle is beautiful in my mind.

A jungle is green with lions and tigers, elephants and monkeys, bright birds.

A jungle smells of heat... coconut oil, eucalyptus.

This is not a jungle. This is like people growing from mud and human waste... shit.

They say they will come to jungle and destroy the school, our mosque, the church, the fields of tents. They will not let us stay here. Kabir tells we will go before that time. We have an arrangement.

One night he wakes and we walk away. 'Quiet, quiet, be silent now, Amir.'

I hold the lemon in my mouth.

'I said three... The agreement was three,' Frozen Man says.

He is Rock Heart and Cargo Man all together – cares only for money.

Mirsa tells him, 'Look, the baby is like carrying nothing.'

Frozen Man says, 'Everything costs money... "nothing" could be very costly if it cries.'

'I will feed her,' Mirsa tells... but Mirsa has no milk left.

Kabir and Mirsa they pay for me because they know my mother and father, because with everything that has happened to them, they have not let the poison enter in their blood.

Mirsa says to me, 'Amir. You will bring us good fortune, Inshallah.'

Frozen Man closes the door of giant fridge, slams it, locks it. He tells us to be quiet 'like nothing'. I show him lemon in my mouth. He looks to me like I am idiot boy, but I suck on hate for him.

Sucking lemon harder, gum is bleeding. Blood is freezing. We hold together to stay warm. We hold together for memory of our village.

> *Mirsa is trying to feed Kalila not to cry*
> *Kalila cries*
> *We are ice breathing*
> *Brain is freezing*
> *Then we are all sleeping*
> *I am not bringing good fortune for Kabir and Mirsa*
> *Kalila stops crying*

Kalila cannot wake
Kalila never wakes
She is frozen in death
We are frozen inside and outside.

*

Reflection George is placing his head in hands and shaking, shaking. 'I am so sorry, Amir. Even I didn't forsee a world this ugly.'
　　'It is not all ugly,' I tell.

*

This is my family now. They finally adopt me and now we are trying to make a place for ourselves in the city.

Mirsa is not my mother
Kabir is not my father
They have no more daughter
I am not their son
This is not my country
But still we are some kind of family together
The lemon from my garden is dried now but I keep it
*　to remember.*

*

Perhaps my story is not easy for you to hear. Maybe some people do not want to hear, but still I think it is one I must tell because I am alive. This is my liberty.

*

Mr Shaw opens the door. 'I'm sorry, Amir. I'm afraid there's not going to be an opportunity for you to speak today. The rules are quite firm. I hope you're not too disappointed. Do you want to stay to see who wins?'
　　Behind me I see the chair is empty.

Reflection has gone.

We walk out into the hall. I turn to see the painting of George Orwell. I did not notice before, this gentle smile. He is looking like gentle man, like my teacher.

'No, Mr Shaw. I don't mind who wins. Let us go home.

THE
DANCER

CHRIS RIDDELL

Patrice Lawrence
THE DANCER

Ghosts flicker in and out of my room. Darkness makes them stronger. Light hides them. They follow me from place to place to place. Last night, I saw one shaped like my brother. I recognised his snake's eyes, wild and wary, his tracksuit heavy with blood and dirt. His mouth open as his scream cut the air. I pulled the blanket over my head and breathed in dead skin.

Today I am underground, with the weight of London pressing down on me. I used to come here with the aunties, some holding my hand as I tried to push the shivering back into my body, some catching me as the rush of people swept me back and away. There are no more aunties. They say I am too old now. I must hold my own hands.

When I first came, I watched faces until one aunty told me it was rude. It was never the white people I studied, though another aunty said it was the white folk that started it, poking and prodding our people until they turned on each other. But that is old history. The white people's voices are like the clatter of the train, noise and rhythm that sink into the background. It's the black people I study, the curve of a nose, the slope of a brow; if there are more than one, I strain hard to hear them talk. There are people from my country in London. From both sides.

I keep my eyes on the ground. A tall, silver suitcase, its tiny wheels shiny with dust. Rows of trainers, black, blue, orange, trailing bright white laces. Black shoes, like funeral shoes, socks crumpling down into the heel. And back to me, leather and beads, toenails painted orange and gold. My last aunty gave me these sandals, passed on from her daughter. At first they were too big, but today they fit. A gift.

The train slows, the door slides open, a march of feet to the escalators and up to the main station. Today should feel different. I should be different. Today I end and begin. Should I choose a new name? Rachel, or Mary, or Sheba, or Hermione? Can I dress in a new skin, weave new hair through mine, change my story?

I walk out of the station and cross the roads that take me towards the river. Yesterday, I was a child. If I had come then, would the trees have been taller? The clouds higher? Would the buttons of my shirt slip into their holes instead of pulling like tangled hair?

There are people dressed for summer, but a cold wind snaps at my skin. Holidaymakers are gathered into their families, phones held high to catch their moments, to plot their routes. A girl leads her man to the food stalls, smile to smile, hand in hand. They pause, talk, move on. They are lovers. They are tourists. What words will they use for me?

I move on too, up the steps and back down towards the river. There is strength beneath the surface. It can pull me down. But the tide is out. Sand, stones, wood, rubbish. Even when the water is high there is no reflection. I cannot lean over and see a woman.

But there is something else, stronger than the Thames. I feel it before I hear it, as if it has broken free and is running along the river wall towards me, looping itself around me and sweeping me back the way it came.

A small stage has been set up between the river and the theatre. People watch and laugh and drink. A band plays and it is their music that has caught me, highlife music, drums, a trumpet, guitars. A woman sings and a man dances around her. Some musicians are white and some are black, their clothes flashing bright as the Sunday church women at the bus stop next to the hostel. They are playing music from Africa. Not my country, not our words. But not English words, neither.

The space in front of the stage is empty, but a woman has come to dance. She is black, older, like a grandmother in a book. Her clothes look like they have been painted on by an artist. They are every colour. They pulse around her as if they are answering the drums.

The people sitting at the tables cheer and clap, but her eyes are closed and she is smiling. The band tilts forward as if they are playing just for her. The song ends and the woman stops moving. She opens her eyes and looks straight at me.

A drumbeat. The trumpet calls. The drum calls back. The woman reaches out her arms and folds the music towards her.

'Come,' she says. 'Come.'

THE MEMORY BOX

Miriam Halahmy
THE MEMORY BOX

Jamal lay in bed, eyes closed. If he stayed like this he could hear his mother's voice in the kitchen; the sound of chickens pecking in the yard, the smell of wood smoke and coffee brewing and it was as though he'd never left.

Then Dave in the next room opened his creaky wardrobe door and Jamal opened his eyes. His mother's voice faded and he was back in Kent, in a village that was nothing like his village back home in Afghanistan. Rain splattered against the window. It was another grey winter's day. He'd been in England six weeks and hadn't seen the sun once.

Another creak as Dave opened his bedroom door to go down to the bathroom.

'Jam, Dave! Ain't you dressed yet?' called a voice from downstairs.

It was Linda, their foster carer.

Jamal swung his legs out of bed and pulled on his school trousers. There was barely room for his feet in the cramped space. The bedroom was so narrow he could touch the walls with both hands, lying in bed. Dave's room was the same. There was no space for a desk even. Jamal did his homework on the bed.

As he padded down the corridor Dave was coming out of the bathroom, his light brown hair damped down with water, green eyes lowered.

Dave was about Jamal's height but his shoulders were always rounded as if in defeat. He hadn't said a word since he'd appeared in the foster home a week ago.

Jamal had arrived home from school that day to see a boy about his age, fourteen, in the kitchen. Linda was making tea. A short, round woman with a pointed nose and straggly blonde hair, Linda didn't look up when Jamal came in.

'Hello,' he said, polite as always.

'All right, Jam,' Linda's voice was sharp as her nose. He'd given up long ago repeating his name for her. 'This is Dave. He's going into the other bedroom.'

'Hello, Dave,' Jamal said.

Dave was standing near the fridge, hands loose by his side, eyes fixed on the ground. He didn't answer.

Now as Jamal finished dressing he heard Dave go out of his room and close the door. He knew the other boy would be waiting on the landing. Grabbing his school bag, he swung it over his shoulder and went out.

'Good morning, Dave,' he said, as he did every morning. Then he led the way downstairs and into the kitchen.

Linda was dishing up pancakes onto a plate on the table and saying, 'Come on, Kelly, eat up. We have to leave in five.'

A ten-year-old girl with a bright red nose and blonde hair done up in two plaits was pulling tissues out of a box.

Spotting Jamal, she grinned and said, 'Bump fists.' She held out her hand, fingers bunched into a tight fist.

Jamal smiled back and tapped her fist with his.

Linda gave a snort and said, 'Kelly's got a cold so I'm driving her to school today. You boys'll be all right.' It wasn't a question.

Kelly's school was right next to the high school but Linda never gave the boys a lift.

The kettle finished boiling and clicked off. Jamal took two mugs, poured in hot water, dropped in teabags and handed Dave a mug.

Dave didn't sit down at the table for breakfast so Jamal didn't either. Linda never offered pancakes. Jamal made black tea and toast for himself and Dave, otherwise the other boy didn't eat.

'Who drinks it black?' Linda had said the first time they met. 'Never heard such a thing.'

'It is how we do at home,' Jamal had said.

'This is your home now.' Linda frowned at him and her daughter, Kelly, giggled.

Jamal stared at his hands.

His social worker, Mel, had brought him to the foster home. Mel was the first person in England who spoke to him like a human being. She didn't ask questions, just explained things in her quiet, clear voice. She understood that he was frightened; his legs couldn't stop shaking after he was arrested.

He'd made it to Dover in the back of a lorry, all the way from the Calais camp. The air was clear and fresh when he'd jumped down onto the quayside, and seagulls were crying overhead. *Now I'm free*, he told himself, but it didn't last. He was arrested before he could run off.

He'd picked up bits of English over three months on the road. In the police station they questioned him for what felt like hours. He kept saying, 'Jamal / fourteen years / asylum seeker / Afghanistan / please, sir / thank you, sir.'

Finally they left him alone in a room until Mel came.

Mel had straight black hair and eyes as soft as his mother's eyes when she'd kissed him goodbye for the last time.

'I'm taking you to a foster family, Jamal,' she told him. 'Linda and Vic Mason. Vic's a taxi driver but Linda doesn't work.

They have a daughter, Kelly, a sweet kid. You'll have your own room and you'll start school next Monday. All right?'

English people said All Right all the time but it didn't always mean the same thing. When Linda said it, or the boys at school grunted a'right to each other, it was just a way of saying hi. Only the boys at school called him 'migrant scum' and shoved him aside. There were a lot of new arrivals like him in Kent and Linda said everyone was fed up with being overrun.

But when Mel said All Right? it was a proper question and she waited to see if you had anything to say back.

Jamal had nodded and said, 'Thank you. Very good.'

He was hopeful back then that a nice English family would take him in; care for him after all those months criss-crossing Europe alone, hungry and scared. He'd done chores for a bowl of rice in more refugee hideouts than he could remember. He still shuddered when the Calais camp came on the news.

Now as Dave finished his tea and took his mug over to the dishwasher, Jamal saw it was raining harder and gave a sigh. He grabbed his backpack. Linda was scraping Kelly's plate in the bin, while the girl zipped up her thick winter coat and pulled her hood up.

'Remember, Mel comes after school,' said Jamal to Linda's back.

Without turning she said, 'Forgot to tell you, Jam. She's ill again. Can't make it. Maybe next week, eh?'

Jamal exchanged glances with Dave. Did he understand? Was that a flicker in his green eyes?

Jamal felt his shoulders droop. Mel had only visited once since he'd arrived in the foster home and that was in the first week. She kept cancelling appointments. Linda said she was ill. He hadn't seen Dave's social worker either. Maybe he didn't have one.

No one cares about asylum kids like us, Jamal told himself as he followed Dave out of the house. They were both wearing thin jackets more suited to summer than the cold, wet English winter. In Afghanistan he'd had a thick coat with a fur collar and a hood that covered his ears in the freezing winter temperatures.

Jamal wanted to tell Mel how they both needed new coats and other clothes for the winter; how Linda locked the kitchen cupboards and never invited them for pancakes; about his radiator that never got warm and, perhaps most important of all, about Dave. He wanted to ask all sorts of questions, like where's he from? Is he Muslim? He didn't look it with his green eyes and light hair and skin but Jamal had met an Arab boy on the road from Syria who looked like that.

No one's on our side, he told himself, turning his collar up against the cold rain and striding down the road, hands shoved in his pockets, already shivering from the cold.

At least they had double maths today. It was Jamal's favourite subject, partly because his poor English didn't matter and partly because the teacher, Mr Begum, was kind to him. He'd told Jamal his family were from India and they knew all about how hard it was to make it in a new country.

'My dad worked as a cleaner for thirty years. He was a teacher back in India but he never got to grips with English,' Mr Begum had told him one morning after the class had gone off to lunch. He'd called Jamal over to praise him for his homework. 'Dad was determined to give me and my brothers a good start. Be patient, Jamal. Things will get better, I promise.'

Now as Jamal arrived in class he wondered if Mr Begum might help with new coats for him and Dave. Maybe he knew who to ask, at least until Mel was better. But what if he phoned Linda up? She would snap at him in her sharp voice with her pointy nose stuck in the air.

Not a good idea, he decided with a sigh.

He'd asked Linda for a phone call home the previous evening. He was feeling so lonely he wanted to call his uncle in Kabul for news of the family.

Linda gave him a shocked look. 'You had a phone call two weeks ago, Jam, don't you remember? I'm not made of money. Perhaps next month.'

What can I expect? he'd told himself, as he went upstairs. It's so expensive to ring Kabul.

'Don't be any trouble, to *anyone*,' his mother had said before he left. 'Don't bring shame on the family.'

I'm trying, he'd told himself, as he lay down in his cold room. *But everything's so hard.*

The rest of the day passed slowly. It was still raining as they walked home and he and Dave let themselves into the house dripping wet.

To Jamal's surprise, Linda came rushing out of the living room and down the hall.

'Here you are, boys. You've got a visitor.' Her eyes were wide, her nose pointing upwards.

Jamal caught Dave's eye but the other boy looked away. *Is it Mel after all?* wondered Jamal.

'Come on,' he said and went into the living room.

A man in his forties, bald head shaved clean and eyes that crinkled at the edges, was sitting on the sofa. He stood up when the boys came in, towering over them, and offered his hand.

Jamal hesitated and then he shook it. The man had a firm grip.

Dave hovered in the doorway and the man gave him a steady look.

'Hello boys. My name's Mark Tiller. I'm your new social worker. Mel's not well. Hope that's OK.'

He turned his gaze on Jamal and Jamal stared back.

Now what? he thought. Before he could say anything, Linda came in with a loaded tray.

She set out steaming cups of tea and plates of cake and biscuits, chattering away. 'So we always have a nice tea about this time, don't we, boys...'

Do we? thought Jamal.

'... Jam, pass Mark the sugar. Dave...' Linda patted the sofa. 'Come on, lovey, sit down.' She grinned over to Mark. 'He's the quiet one.'

Mark levelled his steady gaze at her. Then he looked up at Jamal, who met his eyes and they stared at each other for a few seconds. The room went very quiet. Linda's face was quite red.

'Like being called Jam, do you, Jamal?' Mark's voice was very cool.

Jamal was equally cool. 'My name is Jamal.'

'And Dave?' Mark looked at the other boy, still standing in the doorway, head bent. 'Daoud, isn't it?'

The boy's head rose, his green eyes flashing.

'Daoud? That's your name?' Jamal said. The Arabic word felt good in his mouth.

The other boy didn't answer so Mark said, 'Daoud will speak when he's ready.'

He stood up and went over to the boy. Putting his hand on his shoulder, he said, 'You're from Iraq, aren't you?'

Daoud gave a slow nod.

'And you became separated from your brother on the road?'

Another nod.

Mark patted his shoulder and went and sat back down again. 'I'm trying to find a contact number in Iraq to telephone Daoud's family,' he said. 'When I come next week I'll bring an Arabic interpreter, all right, Linda?'

'Of course, anything we can do for our boys,' Linda said

and her neck was flushed now as well. 'Me and Vic do our best, two big boys eating us out of house and home. Vic's only a taxi driver, you know, we're not made of money and—'

'You receive an allowance for each boy, don't you?' cut in Mark with his cool voice.

Allowance! Jamal let out a gasp. Mark shot him a look.

'How much, please?' Jamal asked in a quiet voice.

'Clothes allowance, food allowance, school uniform, phone calls...' Mark was ticking them off on his fingers.

But Jamal had stopped listening. 'Phone calls! I can call home?'

'As often as you want, mate,' said Mark.

'But... but... please, it is Kabul. Very expensive,' stammered Jamal.

'Doesn't matter, it's policy to keep all children in Care in touch with their family, isn't it, Linda? We explained all of this when you put yourself forward as a foster carer, didn't we? Have you been receiving the allowances into your bank account?'

Linda shrugged and pursed her lips.

It was as if someone had set off a bomb under Jamal. All the anger and pain of the past months shot out as he said, almost shouting, 'Me and Daoud must to have winter coat, we are cold, it rain here all the days, our bedroom cold, no heater and why don't we get same food like Kelly and you!'

He pointed his finger at Linda, who stuck her nose in the air and then, catching sight of Mark's face, lowered her eyes.

Jamal dropped his hand and said in a quieter voice, 'Sorry, Linda, I so missing my family. You and Vic are good, give me bed and food but... but...'

Tears welled in his eyes and his throat closed up. He wanted to sob and sob in his mother's arms. *Will I ever see her again?* he thought, a deep pain in his belly.

Then a hand settled on his shoulder. It was Daoud sending warmth through his T-shirt all the way down to his bones, calming him.

'Things will change from today,' said Mark, giving Linda a hard look. 'Right?'

Linda nodded, her face brick-red, and Jamal almost felt sorry for her. She was not a clever woman, he could see, and she didn't have his mother's kindness.

But she is all I have right now, he thought.

Linda collected cups onto the tray and Mark finished his slice of cake.

Then he said, 'I have something for each of you boys.' He pointed to two small but strong-looking cardboard boxes. Jamal hadn't noticed them before. One was red, one green, and they both had fitted lids.

'They are your Memory Boxes,' said Mark. 'Yours is the red one, Jamal. You can keep all your personal things in there; photos, letters from home, anything you want.'

He stood up. 'Thanks for the tea and cake, Linda. I expect you have a lot to do now.'

Linda nodded. 'I'll take them shopping on Saturday, all right, Jam... I mean Jamal, Da... oud?'

'That is good,' said Jamal.

Linda saw Mark out and then took the tray back to the kitchen.

Jamal picked up the green box and handed it to Daoud. When he picked up the red box, it was heavier. He shook it and something moved.

'Come on,' he said, and Daoud followed him up to his bedroom.

Instead of going into his room as usual, Daoud stood in the doorway and watched Jamal open his box. Inside was a book wrapped in a green cloth.

It can't be, thought Jamal, as a thrill went through him.

He took the book out, laid it carefully on the bed and opened the cloth to reveal a brand new Koran.

Looking up, he saw Daoud's eyes fixed on the book. His face looked as if it was lit from the inside.

So he's Muslim, thought Jamal. Picking up the Koran, he held it out and said, 'Shall we pray?'

Daoud took the book and, moving back, knelt down on the landing carpet. Jamal came out and knelt opposite, not sure what to do next.

But Daoud, the book in his left hand, closed his eyes, put his right hand over his ear and began to chant in a strong, clear voice, '*Allahu akbar... allahu akbar... allahu akbar... ash hadu an la ilaaaha illal Allah...*'

He chants like the Imam back home, thought Jamal, feeling close to tears again. The familiar sound poured over him like warm water, soothing the sadness inside.

Daoud's a Muslim like me, he told himself. For the first time since leaving home, he didn't feel so alone.

Then he felt a hand slip into his. It was Kelly.

'What's it mean?' she whispered.

'God is great. God is great. God is great. I swear there is no other God but Allah,' whispered Jamal back.

'It's beautiful. Will he sing it every day?'

'I hope so.'

The girl was quiet for a moment and then she said, 'Do you think I could have a memory box too?'

'Yes,' said Jamal. 'I'll ask Mark for you.'

They stood together until Daoud had finished. Jamal took the Koran and wrapped it up in the green cloth again. He patted Daoud's arm and gestured that he could take the Koran whenever he wanted.

This is our best memory, he told himself.

Then Kelly said, 'Mum's got a surprise. Come on.'

*

In the kitchen, Linda had laid four places at the table. She waved to the boys to sit down and put a mug of black tea in front of each of them. Then she took a plate from the counter, stacked with pancakes.

Jamal felt his stomach rumble. *Have things changed so much?* he wondered.

Daoud's head was bent.

Picking up a fork, Linda said, 'Two to start with, Jamal?'

Jamal nodded and Kelly pushed the sugar bowl towards him.

'I like cinnamon too but we've run out,' she said.

'Do you want to ring your family tonight, Jamal?' said Linda.

'Thank you,' said Jamal.

Linda gave Daoud a nervous glance. Nodding at his plate, she said, 'Pancakes, Daoud?'

Daoud raised his eyes and then he opened his mouth and said, 'Yes.'

Everyone stared at Daoud for a moment.

Then Kelly cried out, '*Allah* thingy!'

'*Allahu akhbar*,' murmured Daoud. 'God is great.'

'Bump fists, Jamal.' Kelly pointed her closed fist across the table, a broad grin on her face.

Jamal leaned over and bumped his fist. Then he turned to Daoud.

Daoud tapped Jamal's fist with his own. 'Thank you,' he said in his low voice.

'Won't be able to shut him up soon, will we, kids?' Linda said.

Kelly giggled and Linda smiled, her face a bit softer.

Jamal picked up his knife and fork and started to cut his very first pancake in his new country.

Maybe I can make it in England after all, he thought, *and make my family proud.*

Like Mr Begum said, things will get better.

Lucy Popescu
FINDING A VOICE

Yara had always loved writing and now that her English had improved, she joined the group. She wasn't sure if she could describe what had happened to her but she wanted to use her imagination again. To think about stories other than her own.

There were two workshop leaders, both volunteers. Lyn was slim, grey-haired with a kind face. A retired teacher, Yara thought. It later turned out that Lyn was a respected writer and had only taken up teaching in recent years. She had herself been a refugee as a child, but rarely spoke of it. Mai was in her thirties, snub-nosed with unruly blonde hair. She always wore bright red lipstick. During the day, she worked as a teacher at a local school and, after taking a course in therapeutic arts, had formed the writing group for refugees and migrants, found funding and arranged for it to be held in a community centre in Victoria every Wednesday evening.

It was two long bus rides from Yara's home but she had time on her hands while she waited for the British government to decide whether she could stay or not. She was lonely and could go for days without talking to anyone. The group was warm and welcoming. There was always tea, coffee and biscuits.

Occasionally, Yara was baffled by the exercises they were given. Just before Christmas they talked about Robin

Redbreast and mince pies, which contain no meat. Another time they looked at 'The Owl and the Pussycat' by Edward Lear. The two Zimbabwean girls in the group hooted with laughter, but the poem held no meaning for Yara. Sometimes they would read a page of text, an extract from a story or novel, and although Yara tried to keep up, translating the words on her phone, she felt left behind. Often when it was time to write she wasn't sure what was expected of her. The first day, the only words she put on paper were: 'My mind is frozen, like my feelings.' On another occasion she wrote: 'I've lost my voice.' Although as a child she had loved reading books aloud with her mother, now she hated being asked to read from her work at the end of the workshop. She would smile, shyly, and shake her head.

One time they looked at letter-writing. They were each asked what it was like in their country before the internet became widespread. Was their post delivered or did they have to collect their mail from post offices? Did people like to write letters? They explored these questions in pairs and then they were asked to write a letter to a loved one.

Yara hesitated. Who could she write to if all her loved ones were dead?

She thought long and hard before deciding to write to her mother. She wrote in her own language but she knew that she would have to translate the letter later, at home, in order to be able to share and to help improve her English.

Madar Jan,

I miss you so much. It's been a year since we've seen one another. It's been hard but I keep trying to fit in. I'm so sorry that we never got to say goodbye. I hope you will be proud of me. I remember everything you taught me. Every day I praise all those who helped me reach safety. I go through their names in my head and thank each one.

It was a bad crossing. The boat was overcrowded. Many people fell overboard. I saw people drown, children, some were cut by the boat's propellers. I can't describe it. I can't even think about it. I really want to study but I'm not allowed to until I get Leave to Remain. Such strange words – to leave, in order to remain. Instead, I come to these writing classes and they help. There are kind people who visit me and take me on outings. I saw the sea again last week. It was at rest, no longer angry. I love you. I miss you.

I think it is so sad that I will never know what you were like as a child. You were my mother, and you were also like a sister and a best friend. You were all those to me. But what were you like as a child? Stubborn, brave, argumentative, loving? Perhaps these are false impressions. Maybe you were never any of those things, but this is how I think you might have been.

I wasn't with you when you died. You were in the prison hospital. I had left at midday and was at home, alone, trying to catch up on sleep. Qu was allowed to remain overnight when your breathing become laboured. I don't know if you were aware that he was there with you. He rang me at twenty past midnight with the terrible news. We had agreed I would phone round the rest of the family, your friends. I put the phone down and howled. And then I went blank. Had I just spoken to my uncle? Were you really dead? I couldn't quite believe it. I couldn't quite trust myself. I asked myself, 'Is Maman dead?' I was still not sure, so I phoned Qu again and asked him to confirm whether this was true. My poor uncle had to repeat the time and manner of your departure. I pulled myself together and made the calls.

Wasn't it enough that they had taken your life? Did they have to hound me as well? I was only just out of school, starting out as a student. But I was marked. I was your daughter and proud of it. I am still proud to be your daughter. Your best friend Hassan got me the necessary papers. I left three months after your funeral. I am safe, for now.

I love you.

Yara

Yara means courage or strength. Her mother had chosen her name.

It took Yara three days to translate the letter into English. The following week she arrived at the community centre determined to share what she had written. When it came to her turn she started reading. This tiny voice came out. The others strained to hear. Lyn cupped her ear; Mai gestured with her arm for her to raise the volume. She could not. And then as she read back the words in this strange, difficult language, memories of her mother overwhelmed her and she began to cry. She had to stop reading. Her neighbour gave her a tissue, Mai came over to hug her. But it was unbearable. She was torn apart by grief. Yara grabbed her bag and ran from the room.

Three weeks went by before Yara found the strength to return to the group. She knew there was nothing to be ashamed of. Other people had broken down before when writing or talking about home. Everyone greeted her warmly. Lyn took her aside before the session started.

'I was lucky,' she told Yara. 'I was only very small when we came to England and we were made to feel very welcome here. I don't know what has changed in this country but something has and I feel for you. I know it's hard when you think about all that you have lost, but you need to dig deep, find the courage to keep moving on, to find a new life for yourself. Every day it will become a little easier. You'll make friends. Stick with us, don't give up yet.' Yara savoured the advice. Tears came to her eyes. She blinked them away and sat down next to Lyn.

Mai announced that for all those who enjoyed singing, they were going to have a special session inspired by songs from home. Anyone who wanted to could prepare a song from their home country and share it with the group next time. Everyone would be encouraged to join in the singing if there was a tune and a chorus that they could easily pick up.

Yara loved singing and she knew just the song she would pick. Renewed by Lyn's words, she practised all week, carefully transcribing the words into English. She wanted to give copies to Lyn and Mai so that they could understand the meaning of the song.

That day there was terrible traffic, helicopters were flying overhead and police sirens were blaring. Yara's bus was late and when she arrived at the community centre, everyone was already sitting in a semi-circle, ready to start. There were two new members who had already introduced themselves to the group. Yara was nervous. Would she remember all the words? Would her singing let her down? Would that strange, small voice take over again?

A young Eritrean woman went before Yara. Her singing was beautiful and, despite her slight frame, she seemed to reach every register possible for a human voice. Yara listened transfixed. Afterwards, she fidgeted in her seat, flexed her fingers, quietly cleared her throat. Then it was her turn.

She stood, walked towards Mai, turned and faced the group. Everyone smiled at her encouragingly. 'This is a song from my country,' she stuttered and paused. She attempted to sing. But the awful, tiny voice was back. It seemed to rise above her head and she had no control over it. Instead of seeing images from home, she saw the waves rising higher, the boat tipping in the wind, the final capsize. All she could hear were the screams of her companions, the cries of babies, the distress of their mothers. Men and children falling overboard. She remembered the bitter taste of salt on her tongue, the cold slap of water on her skin, the wail of the wind, the splinters from the boat creating tiny crevices in her fingers.

She fought back tears. She realised she would have to abandon the song – her voice was barely audible. She stopped, apologised, took a breath. She remembered her name, Yara, 'courage', and tried to breathe life into the song. Again, the first line was too soft, people were straining to hear her. She continued with the second line, the third and realised with disheartening clarity that she would have to give up. She had lost her voice.

She thought again of her mother, her father. Their home. The early years when Papa had always been there. Then his absences. At first she was told that he was away visiting family. She was seven when they told her the truth. Her father was in prison. He was a political prisoner. Yara had no idea what this meant but she missed him, the scent of him, his prickly stubble as she hugged him. Occasionally he returned, but the time he spent away quickly outnumbered the days he was at home and then he no longer came home. It was just Yara and Maman. She really needed to be able to share this small sliver from her past. A memory. A song, that's all it was.

Yara tried again. And then she heard another voice, like an echo, singing the same words, tracing the same tune, harmonising with her own voice. Sitting directly opposite her was one of the new recruits, a young woman like herself, maybe seventeen years old. She had frizzy brown hair, a pale, anguished face, a broad, generous mouth. Her hair and face were bare like Yara's. She threw her head back and let her voice fly – it joined Yara's mid-flight. Like two birds, they met and danced around together. They fed one another and their two voices rose as one. Suddenly Yara felt a surge in her body: the sound she made filled and vibrated against her entire body. She was singing. Her voice had returned. It soared.

DARK STAR

CHRIS
RIDDELL

David Almond
DARK STAR

Dark Star has lit a fire of driftwood in the circle of stones. He has three fish on a broad flat stone that rests among the flames. They sizzle, blacken, smell delicious.

'You could have one,' he tells me. 'They are nearly done, Louise. They will be delicious.'

'I could bring some bread,' I say.

'Yes.'

So I run to Spinner's Cottage. I get the loaf and a bottle of water left for us by Mrs McTavish and I hurry back again. I sit on the sand. He cuts the bread with a little sharp knife. He lays a fish on a slice for me. A mackerel, my favourite. I nibble the firm, oily flesh, I bite into the bread. Yes, so sweet, so salty, so delicious. So simple. Yes, this is what I want: simplicity, beauty, a simple fish with a beautiful boy. Fish in the sky above, fish in the sea beneath, fish inside my belly.

Then I notice the blood on his brow, a dried trickle beneath a small cut. I point to it.

'What's that?' I ask.

He traces it with his finger, inspects his finger, shrugs.

'Blood,' he says. 'Nothing.'

'What happened?'

'Nothing. It happens sometimes, Louise.'

He points to a scar on his forearm, another on his cheek.

'This in Italy,' he says. 'This on a train in France. It's nothing. What would a life be without wounds and scars?'

I want to ask more but he shakes his head.

'It's nothing, Louise. It's just that some people do not want a wandering boy wandering through them.'

I ponder my own scars. One on my knee where I fell off my bike, one on my nose from chicken pox. And the internal scars, and the everlasting yearning for a lost mother. And the pain that goes with such scars.

'I think you are a sad girl, Louise,' Dark Star says.

'What?' I answer. I've almost forgotten he's there. 'No, of course I'm not.'

He smiles.

'I am in fact a very happy girl,' I say.

'That's good. It is good to be happy.'

And I am. It's true. It is my wandering, weird, mixed-up mind that gives the illusion that I am sad. I love my life, I love my friends, I love this world. And scars help me understand how blessed I am.

There are people ambling past. Over the years, we have come to recognise many of those who live here. A fisherman carries a lobster pot, silhouetted against the darkening sky. He waves and smiles.

'No Dad this year?' he calls.

'Oh, yes!' I answer.

He gives Dark Star a long, hard look, and then moves on.

'Where are you from?' I ask Dark Star.

'From far away, Louise. From somewhere you have never heard of.'

He bites the fish and bread, licks his fingers, swigs the water. He passes the water to me. I swig and try to tell if I can taste him in it.

He offers me the third fish. I decline. He begins to eat.

'I am from the desert,' he says.

The word in this place seems so intense, so out of place.

'The desert?' I echo, and the word feels strong and strange on my tongue and breath. 'Which desert?'

"The Syrian desert."

'Ah, of course I've heard of that.'

'Yes. So have you been there?'

'Oh no.'

'It is where the palms bloom and the sun blazes and the air is dry and the earth is fierce against the feet. And it is not unlike this place.'

'What?'

'It is beautiful. The sky is wide. It opens the soul.'

I look at his meagre possessions: the rucksack, the knife, some clothes. I think of him walking across the wide world all alone.

'The endless sand is like the endless sea,' he says. 'And the sky is endless everywhere. It makes us know that we are very small. And it has its lovely remnants of an ancient age.'

'Are you a refugee?' I ask him.

'Is that what you would like me to be?'

The question embarrasses me. This whole thing embarrasses me.

'No,' I say. 'I don't know.'

He laughs.

'I am a refugee!' he says. 'Help me! Save me!'

He stands up, puts down his food and walks a few steps towards the beach. He casts himself down onto the line of jetsam and he lies sprawled there, as if he's been washed up, as if he's drowned, as if he's dead. He doesn't move. Nor do I. A man walking his dog pauses, recoils, walks on.

Dark Star rises again and returns to me.

'Is that how I should be?' he says. 'Thrown up dead onto the shore by the careless sea? Washed up to be mourned and soon forgotten?'

'Of course not,' I answer.

'How old are you?' he asks.

'Sixteen.'

'Where is the man you were with?'

'My father.'

'Yes, you said that. Your father. He does not look like you.'

'Of course he doesn't look like me!'

I look into Dark Star's eyes. I see something wild there, something of myself there, something of the deer and seal and skylark. I shiver.

'He'll be coming for me soon,' I say.

'Ah, to save you perhaps. To rescue you from the scary stranger. Are you frightened of me?'

'No. I don't know.'

'I am from Syria, from the desert, from the city of Palmyra. Do you know the city of Palmrya?'

'No.'

'Once it was a major city of the world. A place of temples to the sun and moon, and of great archways curving against the desert sky. A place of trade, where all races lived as one. Then it fell as all civilisations can seem to fall. It was destroyed, its people were put to death.'

'That's terrible.'

'The destroyers were the Romans, those thought to be the great civilisers of the ancient world.'

'You lived among the ruins?'

'No, in the modern city by the ruins. The place where tourists stayed when they came to see the great temples and baths and cemeteries that survived, to see the art that was saved from destruction and that lived on through the centuries.'

'It must have been beautiful.'

'Yes. As beautiful as this place, Louise. It was the place where I was born, the place in which I was a child, the place in which I grew.'

He stirs the embers of the fire with a stick.

'And then destruction came again,' he says. 'Bombs fell down on us, tanks and soldiers came. We cannot be allowed to live in peace. We fled like beasts in terror.'

And I remember what happened in this city of Palmyra. The destroyers, blowing up the temples, blasting them to smithereens, turning them to sand and dust.

'Yes,' I gasp. 'I saw it on TV. I saw the temple blown to bits.'

'Ah. Yes. On TV, Louise. You have just remembered. That is good.'

He stirs the embers again. They burn and glow more brightly as the day comes to a close. He throws on a piece of driftwood and it flares to vivid life.

'You are beautiful, Louise,' he says.

I don't know how to answer. I don't know if I should leap to my feet and run from him as a deer would.

'One day,' he continues, 'I will go back to the place of my childhood, just as you come back to Lindisfarne, and it will be a place of happiness and peace again.' He laughs. 'Some would say that is a crazy dream. It is not a crazy dream.'

Suddenly, he stands upon his hands. He walks on them around the upturned boat shed. He jumps up onto the keel of the shed and spreads his arms wide and stands there silhouetted against the sunset.

'I am Dark Star,' he says. 'I am free. I wander the world at will. I go where I wish. Who is there to stop me?'

He leaps down again. He turns a somersault.

'Who is there to stop me, Louise?' he asks.

'Nobody. Not me.'

'That's good. I am Dark Star. I come from an ancient family of tent-makers who make tents for those who roam the valleys and the deserts. My tent is my skin. I go where I will and one day I will go to Palmyra again. Do I frighten you, Louise? Do you think I am wild?'

I cannot speak. I feel my mother's shade nearby. I imagine my stupid father with his stupid woman in her stupid bed. I feel suddenly at home with this strange and beautiful Syrian boy.

The air is becoming chilly as darkness comes on.

My mind is seething, reeling, as darkness comes on.

The sea is still, the island is still.

The complex firmament is studded with the very first stars.

I take the keys from my pocket and unpadlock the door of the upturned boat.

Red light shines through the cracked and dusty window onto the sandy floor, into the strange, baffled silence.

'You can sleep in here tonight, Dark Star,' I say. 'You'll be safe in here.'

He stands at the door with me.

'It's good to be here at last,' he murmurs.

'What do you mean, at last?'

'It is good to be at a home that is like a boat. A boat that is like a tent. Maybe it will carry me back to my Palmrya in my dreams.'

'I could bring you a blanket,' I say.

He shakes his head and takes out a fleece from his rucksack.

'The world's travellers must always be prepared,' he says.

He gazes at me. The late light catches his earrings, his eyes.

'Carpe diem,' I whisper inside myself. 'YOLO, Louise.'

I start to shiver.

I am drawn towards him, but I step away from him.

'Now I have to go,' I tell him.

'Yes?'

'Yes.'

He smiles, steps inside, and I leave him.

I hurry away towards the village, in excitement, and not a little fear.

S. F. Said
THE BIG QUESTIONS

I write children's books because I believe they're the books that change people's lives.

My favourite book as a child was *Watership Down* by Richard Adams. I re-read it as an adult, trying to understand why I'd loved it so much. More than a thrilling adventure story about rabbits, I saw it was a story about the big questions of human life: Who are we? Where do we come from? Where do we belong? How should we live?

I think that's why it meant so much to me. My family's roots are in the Middle East. My ancestors were Iraqi, Egyptian, Kurdish and Circassian Muslims. I grew up in Britain in the seventies, where such origins were unusual. Negotiations around identity, difference and belonging were daily facts of my life. Even my name was an issue. Sabah Falah Said is an ordinary Arabic name, but unpronounceable in English! Whenever it came up, people would question it to such an extent that I ended up using initials.

So when I read *Watership Down* and saw that the hero of the rabbits' myths was called El-ahrairah, it struck a very deep chord. The greatest rabbit who ever lived had an Arabic-sounding name? That gave me what Junot Díaz has described as a feeling of seeing myself reflected; realising my background could be something more than a burden.

A children's book had given me a way to think about myself and my place in the world. So now I put everything I have into writing children's books. I put years and years of work into making each book the best it can possibly be, making them as thrilling as I can, but also filling them with those big questions: Who are we? Where do we come from? Where do we belong? How should we live?

In my first book, *Varjak Paw*, these questions are explored through cats and dogs. Varjak is a cat who makes friends with a dog and learns that a dog can be the best friend a cat could ever have.

My new book, *Phoenix*, is set in a galaxy where humans and aliens are at war. The humans have even built a great spacewall to keep the aliens out. The main characters are a human boy on the run and an alien girl he meets. She's a refugee from the war who has grown up in camps, hated and feared by humans. But they discover that they have more in common than they thought – and together, they might even save the galaxy.

I didn't write *Phoenix* about a specific situation in the real world. I wanted to explore those ideas of identity, difference and belonging that I've been living with all my life, and that I think lie at the roots of so many situations, all over the world.

Things have changed so much since my childhood. People are on the move as never before; hundreds of millions of us now live outside our countries of origin. One response to that is to build walls. But another is to build bridges of understanding – as my characters in *Phoenix* must do to survive.

Young people everywhere are hungry for stories to help them navigate this world. My highest hope is that a book like *Phoenix* might help them think about the world, their experiences of it and other people's experiences, as *Watership Down* helped me. I love the idea that children's books can be bridges connecting people, showing them that however different someone else might be, the things that unite us are greater than those that divide us. And that difference can be a source of richness: something to be celebrated, not feared.

ALIEN

S. F. Said

ALIEN

He ran. They ran. Together. Through the backstreets of the spaceport, they ran together. Round a corner, along an alleyway, and straight into a dead end.

An electrified fence loomed up before them, ten feet tall, with floodlights at the top. A noisy crowd was gathered in front of it. There was no way round it.

They were trapped.

'Join that crowd,' urged Lucky's mother. 'Safety in numbers: it's the only chance.' She pushed him ahead of her into the press of bodies.

ssssshh

The hissing was almost directly above their heads, yet it was still so soft and quiet, Lucky couldn't even be certain it was there. He glanced up. The V-shaped shadow was so big now, it blotted out half the sky.

'Don't look up!' whispered his mother. 'Keep your head down, and we might just get away with this.'

It was so hard; every muscle in his body screamed at him to look at the great V in the night sky, to see what it really was. But he forced himself to look down. He shut his eyes, pulse pounding in his throat as he held his breath... one thousand, two thousand... until the hissing faded away at last, and her grip on his hand relaxed.

'They're gone,' she whispered. 'But that was way too close. We're in trouble, Lucky. We need a flight off this world, and I don't know how...'

She shut her eyes, deep in thought. He risked another quick glance up, and was shocked to see the stars all back in their familiar places. The sky looked totally normal and clear again. No V. No hissing. Like nothing had ever happened.

Did I imagine it? he wondered. *Am I losing my mind?*

The people around him seemed unaware of the shadow that had just passed over them. They were focused instead on something at the front of the crowd, by the fence. Whatever it was, this thing held their full attention.

Puzzled, Lucky edged round the side to get a better view.

In the harsh glare of the floodlights there was a fight taking place. Several men were piling in, kicking at something on the ground, then backing away rapidly. Other men were slamming sticks down at this thing – hitting it, then backing away too. They were shouting, their faces red with anger.

He edged a little closer to see what they were attacking.

Then it roared and reared up on its hind legs, scattering the men—

—and Lucky saw horns, great curving horns, pointing up at the sky—

—and his stomach turned to liquid. His blood ran cold.

Because it was an Alien. The first he'd ever seen in real life.

It was a young male, and he was *big*. He was way bigger than Lucky. He was as big as the biggest man in the crowd. He was muscular, too: a solid wall of muscle, hulking and roaring under the lights, like a nightmare come to life.

He was dressed in a strange coat that looked like it was made of liquid metal, billowing behind him like wings.

Fortunately, his flaming eyes were covered by mirrorshades, but Lucky could see cloven hooves protruding from the bottom of his coat: massive black hooves that could crush a Human head.

But there was only one of him, while there were half a dozen men ranged against him. They piled in again, all at once this time, and forced the Alien down by sheer weight of numbers. The crowd howled their approval: 'Get him! Get him!'

Lucky found himself howling along with them. 'Get them all!' he yelled, his fears boiling up inside him.

'Lucky!' warned his mother. She was shaking her head. She looked appalled.

The men were pinning the Alien down beneath the electrified fence. He was struggling and roaring mightily. It took four of them to hold him there, one on each limb. A fifth was hitting him in the face, again and again. He pummelled the Alien, bloodying his nose. He ripped off the Alien's mirrorshades, revealing eyes of blue fire behind them.

'Call the Shadow Guards!' screamed someone in the crowd.

'No!' said the man who was hitting the Alien. 'I've got a better idea.' From his belt, he pulled a hand cannon. He thrust it against the Alien's head, where the horns met the skull.

'Yes! Yes! Finish him!' the crowd yelled as the men held the huge Alien helpless there on the ground.

Lucky's mother took a deep breath. 'I've got a plan,' she whispered. 'You wait here. Don't watch. This might get ugly.'

Before Lucky could answer, she was moving through the crowd. She moved in the most mesmerising way. The people were packed in tight, but somehow she managed to twist and turn through them, and they just seemed to flow right off her. Yet she herself flowed, like a fish through water, or like water itself; like a tidal wave, gathering speed and momentum as she went.

She made it to the front of the crowd, where the men were holding the Alien down. No one stopped her. No one even touched her as she reached out and took the gun from the man – plucked it out of his hand as if she was taking sweets from a child – and threw it away on the ground.

'What the hell are you doing?' yelled the man.

Lucky was as stunned as anyone. Why was she helping an Alien? Why was she even getting involved?

'Leave him alone,' his mother calmly told the men. 'What's he done to you?'

'Haven't you heard? They just bombed Aries One! They'll kill us all unless we kill them first.'

She shook her head. 'Look at the way he's dressed. He's not in their army. He's a civilian. A peaceful refugee.'

'The only peaceful Alien's a dead Alien,' growled the man.

'For your information,' she said, very softly, 'his people have a name. They call themselves the Axxa—'

'His people eat eyeballs! They worship the stars! They're not even *people*!'

Lucky's mother shook her head again. 'Sometimes,' she said, 'I'm ashamed to be Human. Now *leave him alone!*'

There was silence for a moment. Then the man stood up, fist clenched, face red. 'You're a devil-lover, are you?' he spat. 'Then you'll get the same as they do!'

He drew his fist back to hit Lucky's mother – but she moved first. She moved faster. A blur of motion, she arced aside at exactly the right moment, and the man's fist smashed into the electrified fence behind her. He collapsed in a shower of sparks.

The second man swung at her. But already she was rolling away and coming up again, her long red hair flowing behind her in the night. Moving with astonishing speed, she flicked her feet out, like a scorpion flicking its tail, and unleashed a devastating kick that hit her attacker squarely in the solar plexus. He dropped to the dirt and lay there, pole-axed.

Lucky could barely believe his eyes. His mother was *fighting*! He had no idea why she was doing it, but she was so good! So fast and skilful. And the way she moved – it was like nothing he'd ever seen.

Another man rose to face her. In that moment the Alien seized his chance. There were only two men left on top of him now, and they were distracted by Lucky's mother. With a mighty roar, he lifted them off his limbs and hurled them into the crowd. Then he grabbed the gun she'd thrown away and held it up in the air.

The crowd broke up as people fled, screaming, from the huge horned beast with the cannon in his hands.

The Alien fired a shot into the air above his head. In the chaos and confusion, Lucky rushed to his mother's side as the last of the crowd escaped, shrieking. And now, for the first time, he could clearly see where they were.

It couldn't have been more different to the clean white spaceport terminal. Behind the electrified fence, the only buildings were some filthy-looking shacks and warehouses. There was a big red warning sign on the fence – DANGER: ALIEN REFUGEE CAMP! It looked like the poorest part of town.

Lucky's heart thudded in his throat. Every instinct told him to follow the crowd away to safety, but his mother held him there as the Alien advanced on them. His massive hooves thumped on the ground as he came. His horns glinted in the floodlights; blue fire burned in his eyes.

'It's OK,' Lucky's mother said calmly. 'You're going to put that gun down now, aren't you? Because *from the stars we all came...*'

'*... and to the stars we return!*' said the Alien. He stared at her, the fire in his eyes flashing. 'How do you know that? Who are you?'

'Let's just say I'm a friend,' she replied.

Lucky gaped at them both, speechless. He'd never heard an Alien voice before; you never heard them on the news. He'd always imagined they just roared and snarled like animals. Yet this one sounded... very Human. And for her part, his mother was acting so strangely, he barely recognised her.

'Where's your ship?' she asked the Alien. 'You still have a ship, don't you?'

'Best ship in the galaxy... except she's stuck in Aries, like we are.' The Alien wiped his bloody nose and retrieved his mirrorshades. 'We can't leave this poxy system without our navigation! They took it away from us!'

Lucky's mother nodded. She peered thoughtfully at the refugee camp behind the fence, in the floodlights' glare. 'If someone could help you with that problem,' she said, 'if someone could give you what you need, would you leave Phoenix?'

'Course! Like a shot!'

'Even though the government just suspended space travel? You'd take off without clearance? You'd risk Shadow Guards coming after you?'

'Hell yeah!' roared the Alien, stamping the ground with a hoof. 'Anything to get out of this hole! After what just happened – I wouldn't care who came after me – I'd be gone!'

'Very good,' she said, with quiet satisfaction. 'So here's the deal. We've got what you need. We'll let you use it if, in return, you give us a ride off Phoenix.'

All this time, Lucky had been struggling to understand. How did his mother think they could help an Alien? But this last part was all too clear, and he couldn't believe his ears. '*Whaaaat?*' he cried. 'Is that your plan? You're saying we should go with *him*?!'

'Lucky,' she said sharply. 'Enough.'

'But we're at war with them!' he protested. 'They're the enemy! My father's—'

'Lucky! I said, that's enough.' She turned to the Alien. 'I'm sorry.'

The Alien shrugged. 'Kid's right,' he said. 'What are you asking *me* for when there's all these Human ships in port?'

She glanced up at the night sky. 'This place will be crawling with Shadow Guards in a minute,' she said. 'We need to get out of here, and so do you. I swear, we'll help you get your ship off the ground, but by all the stars, we need your help.' And then she looked the Alien straight in the eye and asked the question: 'Well? Have you got room for a couple of passengers?'

'Aaaah,' groaned the Alien, wiping blood off his face with the back of his hand. 'Look, if it was up to me...' His words tailed off. 'But I've got a captain, see, and the captain... he won't like this. He won't like it one bit. But seeing as you helped me out – seeing as you just saved my skin – well, I guess you better come with me.'

Adam Barnard
LEARNING TO LAUGH AGAIN

In August 2017 I heard about a plan to take a group of teenage refugees to a farm in Devon for a sort of therapeutic activity holiday. Journalistic synapses firing, I set about persuading the organisers to let me come, and chronicled the experience in the following article, published in *The Times* on Monday, 4 September 2017, under the headline: 'Where teenage refugees learn to laugh again'.

So far, so normal – though it's fair to say that my twenty-four hours on the farm, and the often harrowing stories that the young people told me, made a considerable impression. Shortly after the article was published, however, something happened that caused me to reflect on my encounter in a new light. Have a read; I'll see you on the other side.

Where teenage refugees learn to laugh again
On an organic farm somewhere on the eastern fringes of Devon, on a clear, starry summer night, a dozen teenage boys are dancing around a campfire. Their hands rest on each other's shoulders; their feet kick into the air. The boys are from Syria, Eritrea, Afghanistan, Iraq – a roll call of places beset by hardship, persecution and war. But they are euphorically happy. Kurdish pop music blares from a smartphone. One of the group, Khalid, a smiling, softly spoken Egyptian, turned eighteen today. We're celebrating.

Across the fire, perched on a log, watching, is Romy Fraser, whose farm we are on. In a previous life Fraser founded and ran Neal's Yard Remedies, the wholesomely herbal health and beauty store. She sold her stake in 2005; three years later, she bought 300 acres in Devon and set about constructing a co-operative, self-sustaining farm and education centre. It is on this land – Trill Farm – that we now sit.

Or dance. For Fraser has opened Trill Farm to a cohort of young refugees who have survived unimaginably brutal journeys, over many months and without their families, from their troubled homelands to Britain.

'This is what I bought the farm for,' Fraser tells me as we tour grounds that produce everything from organic food to handcrafted oak chopping boards. She speaks quietly in short bursts punctuated by thoughtful pauses. 'I want to support people connecting with nature, connecting with themselves, connecting with each other. Having the kids here... It's meant a sense of fulfilling its purpose.'

In a packed, five-day programme that covers the breadth of her land, Fraser's young guests feed animals, pick vegetables, fly owls, tend bees, blend herbs, fire pots, bake bread... Fraser describes it as part activity holiday, part learning experience, part therapy.

Arriving midway through the stay, my initial impression is of a typical assembly of mid-to-late teenage boys. Slipping in and out of activities, they joke, play-fight and smooth carefully waxed hair. As they congregate around some picnic tables in one of several courtyards edged by Trill's seventeenth-century stone buildings, all that stands out is their broken English. With eight native tongues between twelve of them, it is the only common language.

'What is, the newspaper?' one asks me. 'Has it sudoku?'

Another: 'Are you on Instagram?'

A third – looking up from the remarkably slick wooden

stool he has constructed – makes to shake my hand only to
reveal that he is wearing a glove covered in wood polish.

It is, Fraser tells me – and everyone I speak to backs her
up – a transformation. Two days earlier, on arrival, they
were quiet, wary, sticking together. 'Now,' chimes in Graham
Newing, a widely exhibited potter and friend of Fraser's who
is leading pot throwing and mug firing, 'they are awake.'

Awake – and a lot of fun. At a herbal-product-making
class, a Syrian boy raises his hand: 'Do you have a recipe for
make girl come for your heart?'

They're also disarmingly conscientious. After a
communal dinner – which became the impromptu
celebration of Khalid's birthday, complete with gifts from
the Trill Farm shop – the boys fight each other to clear the
plates and scrub the table. They won't let me, or any adult,
help. An Ethiopian boy teases an Eritrean boy about who
is lazier – a classic point of bantering rivalry between their
two nations.

Beneath the ebullience, however, is a palpable sadness.
Under the tutelage of Newing – the potter – the boys have
been making mugs to fire in the kiln. He asked the boys to
inscribe their names; one, whose mother has recently died,
asked Newing to help him write the words 'I love Mum'
instead.

Those with sufficient English are eager to tell their
stories. They make for harrowing listening. At the campfire
that night, Davood, a warm, intense Iranian and the only
other member of the group to have turned eighteen, tells me
that he fled persecution and death threats after converting
from Islam to Christianity. His mother insisted he travel
alone and paid a smuggler to help.

Davood describes a journey so perilous it seems
remarkable that he survived. Shot at by border police as
he crossed the mountains into Turkey on horseback (and
no, he'd never ridden before, and yes, 'it was cool'); nearly

sinking in an overloaded dinghy off the coast of Greece; held captive for ten months in a house in France as smugglers demanded money from a family he had no means to contact ('I wanted to kill myself'); twice risking death in the back of a lorry, first from hypothermia amid frozen fruit, then from oxygen deprivation in an air-tight compartment.

Touchingly, it is the memory of an Afghan man struggling ashore from their stricken dinghy, holding his crying baby above his head as waves crashed around them, which seems to haunt Davood the most. 'I'm crying because the smoke come here,' Davood insists, pointing at the campfire.

Another boy speaks of watching a man die as they trekked, with too little water, across the Sahara. Most, like Davood, made the notorious boat crossing to Italy or Greece. Several, too, recount spells in freezer lorries similar to the one in which seventy-one refugees, including four children, were found dead in Austria two years ago. A charismatic Eritrean youth describes two months in a house in Libya with 300 other migrants – riddled with lice and sleeping on their sides to maximise floor space.

The horrors of the migrant trail are so well documented that the stories feel almost familiar. But to hear them first-hand, from such young mouths, is wrenching.

Less familiar, but also troubling, is what happens after a young refugee enters the system in Britain.

It was in Kingston upon Thames, in Surrey, that police intercepted the lorry in which Davood was hiding. Everything at this point hinges on age, although few refugees carry official documentation. Adults can be held at immigration removal centres while their application for asylum is assessed; younger claimants are put in the care of social services, usually in the county in which first contact was made.

Fraser's dozen guests surfaced in Surrey; all are housed in hostels or with foster families in a series of small towns across the commuter belt. During term-time they can attend English lessons at the nearest suitable college. However, everything stops for the summer holiday. With no one from a similar background in reach and no money to travel, they can do little but sleep, and dwell on the past.

It is this lack of provision that prompted Kayte Cable, a volunteer from Surrey, to organise the trip. Cable is a language teacher; she has taught many of these boys.

'Last year,' she says, 'some of those in my class struggled awfully over the holiday with their mental wellbeing, let alone language. All the work you've done just slides down.'

Clearly, these guys relish being busy. In the vegetable garden I watch two Kurdish lads tear through a row of French bean plants that have finished cropping; others deftly trim crate after crate of freshly dug shallots, which the farm sells to local restaurants. A Syrian boy lifts an empty crate. 'Number five,' he announces.

'These are very strong boys,' says Sam Mukumba, a clay specialist under whose supervision the group has built an outdoor bread oven. Mukumba lives in Gloucester but grew up in Uganda in the time of Idi Amin. Having witnessed atrocities as a child, his family repeatedly displaced by violence, he feels a strong connection with the boys – which is clearly reciprocated. 'They're warriors,' he says. 'I really appreciate their courage to have escaped. Most people would decide to stay, or even commit suicide. They've managed to see another future.'

The morning after the campfire celebration we gather in another field as Karen Stead-Dexter, a falconer at the farm, introduces a succession of birds of prey. 'You can tell if she's unhappy,' she says of Rosa, a European eagle owl with a two-metre wingspan, 'because her tufts will go down. When she's upright she's happy.'

One by one the boys practise holding the bird on their wrists. 'Good,' they chime. 'So good.' Then Stead-Dexter orders them to stand apart and call the bird to each other. And, magically, Rosa starts to fly on command between them.

Fraser watches from a distance with a look of quiet satisfaction. Cable, the English teacher, brushes away a tear. 'It's taken a few days, but this is what we aim for,' she says. 'For them to be boys and not asylum seekers.'

A quiet Afghan boy, at fifteen the youngest in the group, who yesterday told me with simple sadness that his parents are dead, watches next to me. 'I'm so happy,' he says.

That this trip has happened at all is down to a mixture of compassion and social connectedness. Cable had been bemoaning the lack of options for young refugees to Vicki Felgate, a friend who helps to run Elmbridge Can – a community group campaigning for the Surrey borough of Elmbridge to house more refugee families. Felgate knew of Trill Farm through another friend who had worked there. They approached Fraser, who agreed to cover half the cost of the stay. The rest they raised through contacts across the Surrey commuter belt.

Cable and Felgate are spending the week away from their own children to be here. It's something I come across again and again: amid the much-reported racism and xenophobia concerning the migrant crisis, there has emerged a small army of conscientious Brits working quietly but industriously behind the scenes, complementing and building on the limited resources the state makes available for asylum seekers. Now Fraser has been enlisted into their ranks. In every spare moment Fraser, Cable and Felgate swap ideas for how to make this happen again.

'Whether it's Grenfell Tower or refugees, what has been extraordinary is the amount of goodwill,' says Fraser. 'We hear so much about how horrible people are. But the vast majority of people are compassionate and kind. They don't want to be alienated from the world.'

Khalid, the Egyptian whose eighteenth birthday we celebrated (it was, he says, the best birthday he has had), tells me – in part through broken English, in part by pointing at his head – that he had been going 'crazy' cooped up in a hostel all summer. Now, he says he feels like himself again. 'I come here, I change. I am happy here.'

'I don't want to leave,' says Davood, the Iranian. 'It help me a lot to find peace, to relax. Help isn't just with money or house, you need someone to care about you.'

Among the group, I get a sense of focus switching from past to present – and even future. 'I don't want to remember my past,' says the boy from Eritrea. 'I want to move on.'

The previous night, as the campfire party draws to a close, I set off ahead with Fraser, walking in darkness back to the farmhouse. We're talking about travel. 'I've been everywhere,' she says, 'but I've always had a special connection with the Middle East. The music of the call to prayer...'

She trails off, another long, reflective pause.

We stop at a gate. Some way behind us, the campfire has been extinguished and the young revellers are following us back. All we can see are the glowing screens of the phones they hold aloft as torches, as this party of teenage refugees find their way in the dark.

Names of refugees have been changed.

*

Less than two weeks after this article was published, on the morning of Friday, 15 September 2017, there was an explosion on a London Underground train at Parsons Green station. Fortunately – if anything about this miserable action can be termed fortunate – the bomb had apparently malfunctioned, failing to detonate with the intended impact. As a result, while a number of people suffered burn injuries – one, at least, quite seriously – and still others were hurt in the rush to safety that followed the explosion, the attack is believed to have caused far less damage – let alone death – than intended. The following day, police arrested an eighteen-year-old male at the ferry port in Dover. He was subsequently charged with attempted murder.

What has all this to do with my article? I made no connection in my mind between these events and the remarkable young people I'd met at Trill Farm. Why should I? I'd written about brave teenagers searching for safety and hope; this atrocity was the work of one or more cruel, brainwashed or deeply messed-up individuals.

Until, that is, certain details began to emerge. The young man arrested in Dover was widely reported to be an Iraqi refugee, who came to Britain aged fifteen, his parents having died in Iraq. He was living with a foster family in a town in Surrey. The foster carers were an elderly couple, hugely admired in their community, who had fostered more than 200 children. They had received MBEs for their work. As well as the suspected bomber, according to reports, a second young man was living in the care of the couple, described by a neighbour as 'very quiet and polite'.

I knew about these remarkable foster carers and their pleasant suburban house; I had heard first-hand an account of their kindness. For that second young man – who was indeed polite and quietly spoken – was one of the twelve I had met, and spoken with, at Trill Farm. He did not mention the other resident of the house; our conversation dealt mainly with his battle to survive the migrant trail, his hopes for the future and his gratitude towards the people who had helped him. Only a little of what he told me made the article: space was limited, and it was decided to focus more on the boys who had turned eighteen.

To be clear, there is absolutely no suggestion that this young man – nor any of the other eleven boys I met at

Trill Farm, some of whom may have known the suspected bomber through attending the same college – were in any way involved, culpable or complicit. Quite the opposite: the coincidental proximity of these young refugees – whose cause touched me and continues to do so – and another young refugee, whose heart had apparently turned murderous, seems only to illustrate that the challenges faced by young refugees in this country are greater and more complex than most of us can imagine.

First, there is the obvious point – whether or not this proves relevant to the case of the Parsons Green bomber – that young refugees are vulnerable targets for radicalisation. They arrive traumatised both by their awful journeys and by the circumstances that necessitated them, having come in many cases from places where Western action or inaction has been part of the problem. Still children, they have missed a part of what we call childhood. Now, they are severed from their families – from the parents, uncles, aunts, grandparents from whom most people derive a sense of identity, morality and purpose, or at least the feeling, as 'Davood' put it in my article, that there are people around you who care about you. Many arrive knowing no one, and speaking little English; over the long summer break – as I discovered, researching my article – they have limited means to see what few friends they have, and too much time alone with troubled thoughts. Those lucky enough to be placed with good foster carers may still feel disconnected in a small town with which they have no affinity. They may also experience the casual xenophobia and everyday racism that continues to run through the capillaries of modern Britain.

None of this, of course, remotely justifies terrorism, murder or other actions that are criminal or which inflict hurt on other people. Short of profound mental illness, moral culpability – especially in a complex action that involved substantial preparation and planning – should be pretty easy to establish. But it is one thing to justify – or fail to justify – behaviour, another to explain it. In America, where a lonely adolescent with access to weaponry is still equated more with nihilistic school shootings than Islamic terrorism, trauma and social isolation have emerged as conditions that foster atrocity.

In my background research on how UASCs (unaccompanied asylum seeking children) are processed by the state, it became clear that there is proportionately little acknowledgement of the trauma they may have suffered – and continue to suffer – let alone strategies for healing. Instead, they must give interview after interview to Home Office officials tasked with probing – with a view to dismantling – every detail of their backstory. Adolescence can be an emotional rollercoaster for a young person from even the most stable background. It is also, with hindsight at least, supposed to be a time of excitement, fun and self-discovery. Instead, for young refugees, the spectre of refusal of asylum – and deportation once they turn eighteen – looms ever larger through their mid-to-late teenage years.

Most refugees, of course, manage to avoid dangerous influences and maintain a grip on their psyche. There is then the question of whether everyone around them can do likewise. It is a peril that the boy who shared housing with the suspected bomber knows only too well. Those whom mere fate – the twin coincidences of when they reached British soil, and that they entered the system in Surrey and not Kent or Essex or Suffolk – has placed near a suspected terrorist, risk being scarred – or tarred – by association. At the very least, they will face a fresh wave of questioning, notional witnesses forever on the cusp of suspicion; their lives are upended yet again and what progress they have made psychologically might be unravelled. Of the seven – predominantly young – men arrested in connection with the Parsons Green attack, six were released without charge.

It becomes another trauma – to stack on top of existing traumas – that a refugee in the orbit of a malefactor must bear. One more layer of risk in a situation where the odds of surviving, and thriving, are already stacked against you. What woeful irony: to have come here for safety from violence and oppression, only to find yourself caught up – even by indirect association – in a fresh act of war. And now the xenophobia and discrimination you might have hoped to play your own small part in countering, by working hard and becoming a model immigrant citizen, have just been fed and bloated further.

Those prolific, elderly foster carers – splashed across the media, banished from their home as police combed it for evidence, the operation concealed behind vast metal barriers like the perimeter of a wartime prison camp – will not, one suspects, foster again. What a sad twilight to a lifetime of doing good. And what of others who might have looked to their example and thought: I could do the same? What of programmes like the brilliant, nascent scheme at Trill Farm? One can only hope that they retain both impetus and support. We need them more than ever.

ON THE
EXISTING
STATE OF
THINGS

CHRIS
RIDDELL

Simon Armitage

ON THE EXISTING STATE OF THINGS

from Virgil, The Aeneid, Book VI

Then to those shores
that Charon patrols, stalking the quayside,
haunting beach and bay, harbourmaster and ferryman.
With a straggly grey beard under his bloodshot eyes
and a money-bag slung from his bony shoulder
he tacks and jibes, tunes the outboard motor,
herding his cargo into a rusty hull,
old in years but a tireless God of the grave.

Here a pitiful mob crowded the strand:
husbands and wives, the drained dishevelled forms
of the once-proud, bewildered children,
pale daughters and sons pulled from rubble and ash,
men and women holed by sniper rounds.

So many souls, countless as dry leaves
loosened by frost, spinning through autumn woods,
or like flocking birds that darken a clear sky,
migrating seaward looking for greener worlds.
They lined the banks begging to be next to cross,
arms stretched towards a distant coast.
But Charon trafficked as he pleased, first these, then those,
ordering others to stand back from the boat.

*

And there among them the ghost of Palinurus.
Sailing at night from Libya, piloting north,
transfixed by tail-lights bound for Munich and Heathrow
he'd slipped from the stern and gone down in the wake.
Seeing his mournful shape among those shades
Aeneas called out, 'Palinurus, answer me;
which God tipped the Mediterranean into your lungs?'
And the dead sailor replied, 'No God, captain.
It was my one job to chart a course by the stars
but during a sudden squall the tiller sheared off,
fell away behind with me hanging on.
And even half-drowned I cared less for myself
than I did for the vessel and those still sailing on,
adrift in the dark without helmsman or helm,
in the heaving ocean, through valleys of waves.

For three nights in weather out of the south
I was swept along by currents and gale-force winds,
then next dawn, pitched high by the swell,
I caught a glimpse of Italy's jagged peaks.
I swam stroke by stroke, trod water, swam again
till I felt shingle underfoot, sand between my toes.
But sheer cliffs and savage rocks defeated me;
in heavy waterlogged clothes I hung on by my nails
till cold and weakness prised my fingers from the stone.

The tide owns me now. Where day-glo life-vests
lie beached and disembodied at first light
I roll in the white surf at the water's edge.
Comrade, throw soil over my washed-out flesh
or offer your hand and pull my body aboard,
land me where I can rest in peace in the earth.'

BIOGRAPHIES

Hassan Abdulrazzak is an award-winning playwright of Iraqi origin, born in Prague and living in London. His plays include *Baghdad Wedding, The Prophet, Love, Bombs and Apples* and *And Here I Am.* He was also commissioned by the Kevin Spacey Foundation to write *Dhow Under the Sun*, a play dealing with the concerns of young refugees, performed by thirty-five young actors selected from all over the Middle East. Hassan is currently writing a feature film for New Century about the plight of young girls who face the prospect of FGM (Female Genital Mutilation).

David Almond is the author of *Skellig, My Name is Mina, The Savage, The Tightrope Walkers, A Song for Ella Grey, The Tale of Angelino Brown* and many other novels, stories, picture books, songs, opera librettos and plays. His work is translated into forty languages, and is widely adapted for stage and screen. His major awards include the Carnegie Medal, two Whitbread Awards, the Eleanor Farjeon Award, the Michael L. Printz Award (USA), Le Prix Sorcières (France) and the Guardian Children's Fiction Prize. In 2010 he won the Hans Christian Andersen Award, the world's most prestigious prize for children's authors. He is Professor of Creative Writing at Bath Spa University and lives in Newcastle upon Tyne. His new novel, *The Colour of the Sun*, and a picture book, *The Dam*, is published in 2018.

Moniza Alvi was born in Pakistan and grew up in Hertfordshire. Her books include *At the Time of Partition*

(Bloodaxe Books, 2013), a book-length poem that focuses on the partition of India and Pakistan and was shortlisted for the T. S. Eliot Prize; *Homesick for the Earth* (Bloodaxe Books, 2011); *Europa* (Bloodaxe Books, 2008); and *Split World: Poems 1990–2005* (Bloodaxe Books, 2008), which includes poems from her five previous collections. A new collection, *Blackbird, Bye Bye*, is in preparation. She lives in Norfolk where she tutors for the Poetry School.

Simon Armitage is Professor of Poetry at the University of Leeds and the current Oxford Professor of Poetry. His latest collection is *The Unaccompanied* (Faber & Faber, 2017). 'On the Existing State of Things' is a reworking of a section from Book VI of Virgil's *The Aeneid*.

Adam Barnard is a playwright, theatre director and journalist whose work is often for, with or about young people. He was previously joint artistic director of Company of Angels (now Boundless Theatre), one of the UK's foremost producers of theatre for young audiences. His plays include *buckets, Closer Scrutiny, Invisible* and *Too Small to Be a Planet*, which was nominated for the 2016 Deutscher Kindertheaterpreis (German children's theatre prize). He has directed, and had his plays produced, across the UK and internationally. A series of short films he wrote and directed for the Equality and Human Rights Commission has been seen by more than a million young people across Britain.

Tracy Brabin has written on a number of TV series including *Shameless, Heartbeat* and three series of *Tracy Beaker* including the Tracy Beaker Children in Need special. She was also a member of the writing team on *Hollyoaks* for three years and was on the writing team of *Seacht* – nominee for Teen Series of the Year, Northern Ireland Film and TV Awards. Early on in her acting career, she spent over five years working in Theatre in Education and was series presenter of *Corners*, a BBC show that was pitched as kids' *Tomorrow's World*. She volunteered with Freedom from Torture's Write to Life group for three years. Tracy is the Member of Parliament for Batley and Spen and Shadow Minister for Early Years.

Tony Bradman has written poetry and picture books, short and long fiction and educational books and plays. Highlights from 2017 include *Anglo-Saxon Boy* (Walker Books), a middle-grade novel about the family squabbles behind the story of the Battle of Hastings in 1066; *Revolt Against the Romans* (Bloomsbury Educational), a story about a Roman boy who finds himself a hostage in the great conflict between the Celts and the Roman Empire; and *The Greatest Stories Ever Told* (Orchard), a collection of re-tellings illustrated by Tony Ross.

Sita Brahmachari writes novels, plays and short stories. In 2011 she won the Waterstones Children's Book Prize for her debut novel, *Artichoke Hearts*. Her subsequent four novels for Macmillan Children's Books, *Jasmine Skies, Kite Spirit, Red Leaves* and *Tender Earth*, have been variously nominated for the Carnegie Prize, UKLA book award, and endorsed by the Reading Agency and Amnesty International UK. Sita has written three celebrated titles for Barrington Stoke Publishers, *Brace Mouth, False Teeth, Car Wash Wish* and *Worry Angels*, and contributed to anthologies including *Here I Stand* for Amnesty and *I'll Be Home for Christmas* for Crisis and Stripes Publishing. Sita's plays include *Lyrical MC* and *The Arrival* (Tamasha Theatre Company, 2013). She is currently Writer in Residence at Islington Centre for Refugees and Migrants and an Amnesty Ambassador.

Eoin Colfer is the author of the internationally bestselling *Artemis Fowl* books. Other titles include *The Wish List, The Supernaturalist, Airman, WARP* and the Legends series for younger readers. Eoin's books have won numerous awards including The British Children's Book of the Year. The BBC made a hit series based on his book *Half Moon Investigations.* Eoin's collaboration with acclaimed Belfast artist Oliver Jeffers, *Imaginary Fred*, won the Irish Children's Book of the Year in 2015. For the theatre Eoin has written the books for the musicals *The Lords of Love, Bellebottoms* and *Noël,* and scripts for the plays *Holy Mary* and *My Real Life.* His most recent graphic novel is *Illegal* with long-time friends and collaborators Andrew Donkin and Giovanni Rigano.

Brian Conaghan's novels include *The Boy Who Made it Rain,* published in 2011; *When Mr Dog Bites,* which was shortlisted for the Carnegie Medal in 2015, attracting both praise and controversy for its honest, moving and humorous depiction of a teenage boy with Tourette's syndrome; *The Bombs That Brought Us Together,* which won the 2016 Costa Children's Book Award; and verse novel *We Come Apart,* co-authored with Sarah Crossan. His most recent book is *The Weight of a Thousand Feathers,* which deals with euthanasia and young carers. Brian was born and raised in the Scottish town of Coatbridge but now lives in Dublin.

Kit de Waal writes novels, short stories and flash fiction for which she has won numerous awards. Her debut novel, *My Name Is Leon,* won the Kerry Group Irish Novel of the Year Award and was shortlisted for the Costa Debut Novel Award, the British Book Awards Debut and the Desmond Elliott Prize. In 2016, she founded the Kit de Waal Scholarship at Birkbeck University.

Fiona Dunbar is the bestselling author of the Lulu Baker trilogy, about a girl with a magic recipe book, which was adapted for TV as *Jinx*. Her other books include the dystopian Silk Sisters trilogy and the Kitty Slade series of ghostly mystery stories. Her career in children's books began with writing and illustrating picture books. In 2016 she ran an online auction that raised £24,000 to help refugees. She is also an occasional volunteer at a refugee centre in Athens.

Miriam Halahmy publishes novels for children and teens. Her debut Young Adult novel *Hidden*, published in 2011, tells the story of two teens who pull an asylum seeker out of the sea and hide him to save him from being deported. *Hidden* was longlisted for the Carnegie Medal, has been adapted for the stage and will tour in 2018. Miriam has published three further YA novels, *Illegal*, *Stuffed* and *Behind Closed Doors*. Her middle-grade book, *The Emergency Zoo* (2016), tells an unknown story of pets in the Second World War. Miriam was a teacher for twenty-five years in London and has a particular interest in the plight of asylum seekers. Miriam believes that all young people have a future and that reading helps to provide a route map forward.

Peter Kalu's Young Adult novels, *Silent Striker*, *Being Me* and *Zombie XI*, have been published recently by HopeRoad. His short story 'Getting Home (The Proofreader's Sigh)' can be found in the 2015 Peepal Tree short story collection *Closure*. Among his other publications are the romantic comedy *Diary of a Househusband*, and the science fiction novel *Black Star Rising*. You can find out more about Pete at www.peterkalu.com. His twitter handle is @peterkalu.

Judith Kerr was born in Berlin in 1923 but escaped from Hitler's Germany with her parents and brother in 1933 when she was nine years old. Judith wrote about her experiences in her classic autobiographical story, *When Hitler Stole Pink Rabbit*, which – along with *Bombs on Aunt Dainty* and *A Small Person Far Away* – forms part of the *Out of the Hitler Time* trilogy. *The Tiger Who Came to Tea* was Judith's first picture book, published in 1968. She is also renowned for her feline creation, Mog. In 2015 Mog took to the screen in a major Christmas advertising campaign, highlighting the importance of sharing at Christmas. The accompanying book, *Mog's Christmas Calamity*, helped raise funds for Save the Children to improve child literacy across the UK. Her latest picture book, *Katinka's Tail*, was published in October 2017. In 2012 she was awarded an OBE for services to children's literature and in 2016 she was awarded the BookTrust Lifetime Achievement Award.

Patrice Lawrence is an award-winning writer of stories for children and young people. *Orangeboy*, her debut novel for young adults, was shortlisted for the Costa Children's Book Award, won the Bookseller YA Prize and Waterstones Prize for Older Children's Fiction, and has been shortlisted for many regional awards. *Indigo Donut*, her second YA novel, was one of *The Times* top children's books in 2017. Both books have been nominated for the Carnegie Award. Patrice has worked for many organisations promoting social justice and equality. @LawrencePatrice

Michael Morpurgo is one of the UK's best-loved authors and storytellers. He was appointed Children's Laureate in May 2003. He was awarded an OBE for services to literature in the Queen's Birthday Honours in 2007. He has written over 130 books including *Kensuke's Kingdom* and *Private Peaceful*. Many of Michael's books have been adapted for the stage, including *I Believe in Unicorns*, *The Mozart Question* and the National Theatre's multi-award-winning production of *War Horse*. The film of *War Horse* directed by Steven Spielberg was released in January 2012. Michael's latest book is *Toto: The Dog-Gone Amazing Story of the Wizard of Oz*, published in September 2017.

Anna Perera is the product of three islands with an Irish mother and Sri Lankan father. Born in the UK, she lives in London. An ex-English teacher, she spent a few years running a unit for excluded teenage boys, has an MA in Writing for Children and published six books, including the critically acclaimed *Guantanamo Boy*, which was translated into more than a dozen languages, was shortlisted for the Costa Children's Book Award and the Branford Boase Award, and was nominated for the Carnegie Medal and numerous other awards. The book was adapted into a play and performed in London and regional theatres. *The Glass Collector* was also nominated for the Carnegie Medal. Anna gives talks, delivers workshops for schools here and abroad and for asylum seekers in London. Last year she helped out at the Calais refugee camp.

Lucy Popescu is a writer, editor and arts critic with a background in human rights. She was director of English PEN's Writers in Prison Committee from 1991 to 2006 and currently volunteers with Freedom from Torture's creative writing group, Write to Life. Lucy edited *A Country of Refuge*, an anthology of writing on asylum seekers, published by Unbound in 2016. She previously edited Freedom from Torture's collection of refugee writing *Body Maps* (2011) and the PEN anthology *Another Sky* (2007). *The Good Tourist*, her book about human rights and ethical travel, was published in 2008.

Christine Pullein-Thompson was a prolific pony book author. She has over 100 books to her name and has been translated into twelve languages. Christine and her sisters Diana and Josephine wrote their first book together, *It Began with Picotee*, which was published in 1946. Christine married Julian Popescu, and a family visit to Romania, before the 1989 revolution, inspired her to write *Across the Frontier*. Christine continued to write until her death in 2005.

Bali Rai is the multi-award-winning author of over thirty young adult, teen and children's books. His culturally diverse writing often pushes boundaries and tackles a variety of issues. This has made his writing extremely popular in schools across the world. He is also passionate about the promotion of literacy and reading for pleasure. His latest book, *Tales from India*, is a collection of folk tales rewritten for the modern reader.

Sue Reid writes historical fiction and non-fiction for children and young adults. She began her career writing short stories for BBC Schools Radio. She has had eleven books published, several for Scholastic's popular My Story series (including *Mill Girl* and *Pompeii*). Recently published books include a story for younger children, *Tutankhamun's Tomb*, and *Spotlight on Russia*.

Chris Riddell is the creator of an extraordinary range of books which have won many illustration awards, including the UNESCO Prize, the Greenaway Medal (on three occasions) and the Hay Festival Medal for Illustration. His work includes *Ottoline* titles, and the Goth Girl series, the first book of which won the Costa Children's Book Award. Chris has also achieved global success through his *New York Times* bestselling collaboration on *The Edge*

Chronicles with Paul Stewart and through his illustrated works with other high-profile figures including Neil Gaiman and the comedian Russell Brand. Chris was the Waterstones Children's Laureate from 2015 to 2017, and was appointed Book Trust's first official ambassador in 2017. He lives and works in Brighton.

S. F. Said was born in Lebanon but has lived in London since he was two years old. His first book, *Varjak Paw* (2003), won the Smarties Prize for Children's Literature. It has since been adapted as a stage play and an opera, and a film version is in development. The sequel, *The Outlaw Varjak Paw* (2005), won the Blue Peter Book of the Year. His third book, *Phoenix* (2013), was selected to represent the UK on the IBBY International Honour Book List, shortlisted for the Guardian Children's Fiction Award, and nominated for both the Carnegie and Kate Greenaway Medals. He is currently working on a book called *Tyger*, and has written widely on children's and young adult literature for both the *Guardian* and the *Daily Telegraph*. His website is www.sfsaid.com and his twitter handle is @whatSFSaid

Jon Walter is a former photojournalist with a special interest in social welfare issues. His debut middle-grade novel, *Close to the Wind*, was chosen as the *Sunday Times* Children's Book of the Week. *My Name is Not Friday*, his young adult debut, was shortlisted for the Guardian Children's Fiction Prize. He lives in East Sussex with his family.

WHAT YOU CAN DO &
WHO TO SUPPORT

Counterpoint Arts is a leading national organisation in the field of arts, migration and social change. Their mission is to support and produce the arts by and about migrants and refugees, seeking to ensure that their contributions are recognised and welcomed within British arts, history and culture. http://counterpointsarts.org.uk/

Freedom from Torture provides counselling, group therapy and ongoing support. They also run the creative writing group Write to Life. They provide expert medical assessments to support survivors' asylum claims, and use their expertise and evidence to protect and promote survivors' rights and hold torturers to account. https://www.freedomfromtorture.org/

Phone Credit for Refugees and Displaced People is a grassroots organisation helps refugees maintain links to their families. Members of the Facebook group can respond directly to an individual's request for help, sending them £20 via the group to top up their phone. https://www.facebook.com/credit4refugees/

Refugee Action offers help and advice for refugees and asylum seekers on issues including the asylum process and how to access support. http://www.refugee-action.org.uk/

Refugees Welcome helps civil society groups and members of the public coordinate their activities and act together to show that the UK is #ReadyAndWilling and that this is a place which says clearly #refugeeswelcome. http://www.refugees-welcome.org.uk/

Safe Passage exists to help unaccompanied child refugees and vulnerable adults find safe, legal routes to sanctuary. They have reunited unaccompanied asylum-seeking children from France, Greece, Italy, Germany, Belgium, Bulgaria and Syria with their relatives. For those clients who arrive in the UK, they also support their transition to a new life. http://safepassage.org.uk/

Sponsor Refugees is a project of Citizens UK that organises communities to act together for power, social justice and the common good. Their vision is one in which many more people fleeing conflict and persecution are able to build a new life in safety and security in the UK thanks to community groups sponsoring them. They work with partners, including the UK government, to increase the number of groups who sponsor refugees and to embed community sponsorship as a key element of refugee protection in this country. http://www.sponsorrefugees.org

The Helen Bamber Foundation (HBF) is a human rights charity based in London that was founded by Helen Bamber in 2005. Their specialist team of therapists, doctors and legal experts hold an international reputation for providing therapeutic care, medical consultation, legal protection and practical support to survivors of human rights violations. http://www.helenbamber.org/

The Migrant Children's Project (MCP), delivered by Coram Children's Legal Centre (CCLC), promotes the rights of all refugee and migrant children, young people and families, and works to ensure that they receive the protection and support they need whether they are unaccompanied or in a family. http://www.coram.org.uk/how-we-do-it/upholding-childrens-rights/migrant-childrens-project

The Red Cross works with young asylum seekers and refugees, aged fifteen up to twenty-five years. Some of these young people are unaccompanied or separated from their family. When they turn eighteen, the complexities of changing support and not knowing if they can stay in the UK can leave many living in limbo. Others do not hold the right legal documents – and risk being processed as an adult if they cannot prove their age. They are all seeking safety in a new country and culture and may feel vulnerable and confused. http://www.redcross.org.uk/What-we-do/Refugee-support/Support-for-young-refugees

The Refugee Council has been helping refugees and asylum seekers for over sixty years. Many refugees have lost everything, and their lives will never return to normal.
The Council offers practical support and advice throughout their journey in the UK and helps refugees rebuild their lives. https://www.refugeecouncil.org.uk/

Wonder Foundation is a women-led charity dedicated to empowering vulnerable people through education. They work worldwide helping women, girls and their families access the education and support they need to exit poverty, for good. http://wonderfoundation.org.uk/refugees

ACKNOWLEDGEMENTS

My heartfelt thanks to the wonderful contributors who have made this anthology and all those who actively supported the crowdfunding. Thank you to Chris Riddell for original illustrations and Haymanot Tesfa for the evocative book cover. I am hugely grateful for the early and generous support of Jeanne Coker, Michaela Fyson and David Holman. I'd also like to acknowledge promotional support from Counterpoint Arts, Freedom from Torture and the *Literary Review*. Thanks also to Margaret Barnard, Louise Cross, Faz Fazali, Tracey Lee, Tim Melvin, Philippa Perry, Cheryl Pierce, Andrea Rippon, Sunny Singh, Liz Stokes, Caroline Williams and my colleagues and friends at Write to Life. Thanks to Mark Bowsher, who produced my pitch video, and all at Unbound, particularly DeAndra Lupu, Philip Connor, Georgia Odd, Amy Winchester and Jimmy Leach.

Interview with Judith Kerr © Judith Kerr, Lucy Popescu, 2018

'The Dancer' © Patrice Lawrence, 2018

'The Little Red Train' and 'Locked Up' © Michael Morpurgo, from *Shadow*, HarperCollins, 2010

'Gowsika Auntie' © Anna Perera, 2018

'Finding a Voice' © Lucy Popescu, 2018

'I Want the Truth' © Christine Pullein-Thompson, extract from *Across the Frontier*, originally published by Andersen Press Limited, 1990

'The Mermaid' © Bali Rai, 2018

'Our Bridge to Freedom' © Sue Reid, 2018

'The Big Questions' © S. F. Said, originally published by the Children's Book Council, http://www.cbcdiversity.com/post/152645324488/the-big-questions

'Alien' © S. F. Said, from *Phoenix* by S. F. Said, published by David Fickling Books. Reproduced by permission of The Random House Group Ltd. © 2013

'Every Day Is Christmas...' © Jon Walter, 2018

Unbound is the world's first crowdfunding publisher, established in 2011.

We believe that wonderful things can happen when you clear a path for people who share a passion. That's why we've built a platform that brings together readers and authors to crowdfund books they believe in – and give fresh ideas that don't fit the traditional mould the chance they deserve.

This book is in your hands because readers made it possible. Everyone who pledged their support is listed below. Join them by visiting unbound.com and supporting a book today.

Timothy Ades
Judith Allnatt
Su Allport
Linda Almond
AMB
Jacqui Ansell
Rebecca Armstrong
Karen Attwood
Maria Banica
Catherine Banner
Margaret Barnard
Jeannette Baxter
Geraldine Beattie (SCLAS)
Sonia Beck
Jakub & Kasia Bijak
Tony Birch
Anna Blasiak
Margaret Bluman
Ruth Boreham
Zamir Borg-Mirza

Sita Brahmachari
Sarah Brown
Adrian Bulley
Clarissa Burden
Sarah Burrell
Nicholas Burton
Darren Butler
Denise Cann
Nick Cannan
Robert Cannan
Chris Chalmers
Robert Chandler
Sarah Chatwin
Stella Chevalier
Claire Collison
Wendy Constance
Michael Coulten
Sarah Coulten
Frances Cox
Alison Criado-Perez

Stewart Cross
David Cundall
Emma Darwin
Sara Davies
Valerie Davies
Ruth Diver
Beatie Edney
Joanna Elding
Liz Evers
Moris Farhi
Saeed Farouky
Benedict Farr
Charles Fernyhough
Rachel Gaffin Fidler
Rose Filippi
Liz Flanagan
Sue and Paddy Foley
HW Freedman
Alison Freegard
Tina Freeth
Clélia-Elsa Froguel
Jean Georges
Ryan Gibberd
Marcelo Gigi
Miranda Gold
Rich Gowing
Lucy Gray
Rosalind Green
Lenore Greensides
Eleanor Griffiths
Ryan GS
Caroline Haastrup-Baptiste
Mark Harris
Claire Hartmann Thompson
Steve Harvey
Carolyn Hayman
Sheila Hayman
Philip Hewitt
Katy Hilditch
Gabi Hill
Joe Hipgrave

Clive Holland
Rosslyn Hudson
Barbara Hungin
Ray Hunter
Investing in People and Culture
Simon Jay
Emily Jeremiah
Stella Kane
Stephen Kelman
Liz Kessler
Abda Khan
Dan Kieran
Georgie King
Alex Kirby
Audrey Kwong
Pierre L'Allier
Katie Lamble
Pamela Lawson
Helen le May
James Lee
Diane Leedham
Chantelle Lewis
Marina Lewycka
Jacqueline Lloyd
Caroline Lodge
Naomi Love
Sally Lovell
Claire Malcolm
Vanessa Marshall
Sarah Martell
Tracey Mathias
Tim Melvin
John Mitchinson
Alice and Stuart Morgan
Marianne Axon Morse
Carlo Navato
Sirkka Neumann
Kevin O'Connor
Jack O'Donnell
Cassie Oakman
Nick Page

Tanya Pardoe
Tracy Paulin
Katie Pearce
Lucy Peck
Becky Penney
Clare Pennington
Libby Pentreath
Cheryl Pierce
Luisa Plaja
Justin Pollard
Philip Popescu
Lauren Price
Evelyn Quek
Ulla Rahbek
Kate Raworth
Deborah Rees
Sioned-Mair Richards
Andrea Rippon
Charlie Robertson
Brandon Robshaw
Caroline Royds
Tom Ryan
Chantal Savignon
Chris Schuler
Ros Schwartz
Elisa Segrave
Emily Sharratt
Sunny Singh
Emi Slater
Ali and Sarah Smith and Wood
Ian Spinney
Nicola Spurr
Amit Srivastava

Catriona Stares
Laura Statham
Henriette B. Stavis
Robin and David Stevens
Rana F. Sweis
Helen Taylor
Joanna Taylor
Anne-Marie and John Temple
Justin Temple
Olivia Temple
Martin Tiller
Daniela and Gavin Toms
Helen Trippier
Robin Tuddenham
Gustavo Vas Falcao
Mark Vent
Sonya von Fischer
Lucy Ward
Tim Waygood
Lee Weatherly
Andrew Weeks
Meg West
Sandra White
Jane Fiona Whytehead Stocker
Mary Wickenden
Caroline Williams
Catherine Williamson
Sophie Winn
Charlie Wise
Siobhan Wolohan
Stephanie Zia
Meike Ziervogel